W9-AHU-018

A Praed Street Dossier

Two views of the real No. 7B Praed Street, London, taken by Ian M. Law. On the left—the front of the building from across the street; on the right, a close-up of entrance.

A Praed Street Dossier

By
AUGUST DERLETH

With Illustrations
by
Frank Utpatel

Mycroft & Moran: Publishers Sauk City, Wisconsin
1968

• • •

• • •

With a tip of the deerstalker to

Peter Ruber
Ian M. Law
Luther Norris

for Luther Norris,
Lord Warden of the Pontine Marshes,
Godfather to The Praed Street Irregulars . . .

A Praed Street Dossier

Contents

Illustrations

Solar Pons: Marginalia

The Beginnings of Solar Pons

Pons, Solar, born ca. 1880, in Prague. Son of Asenath Pons, consular official at Prague, and Roberta McIvor Pons; younger brother of Bancroft Stoneham, in His Majesty's Service. Public school education; Oxford *summa cum laude,* 1899. Unmarried. Member: Savile, Diogenes, Athenaeum, Cliff Dwellers, Lambs. Est. private inquiry practise at 7B Praed Street, 1907. British Intelligence, World War I, II. Monographs: *An Inquiry into the Nan-Matal Ruins of Ponape* (1905); *A Logical Approach to the Science of Ratiocination* (1917); *The Chess Problem and the State of Mind* (1919); *The Inductive Process* (1921); *On the Value of Circumstantial Evidence* (1925); *An Examination of the Cthulhu Cult and Others* (1931). Widely traveled. Residences: New York, Chicago, Paris, Vienna, Prague, Rome, 7B Praed Street, London, W. 2. Telephone: Ambassador 10000.

THIS IS WHAT one reads of him today, but it was not always thus. As a matter of fact, even this much information was not known about Solar Pons until close to two decades ago, when Anthony Boucher pressed me for it, and I had to examine the chronicles to discover these facts.

Solar Pons came into being out of Sherlock Holmes, just as Holmes came out of C. Auguste Dupin, all chronicled data about Dr. Joseph Bell of Edinburgh University to the contrary. In a sense, Sherlock Holmes *is* C. Auguste Dupin. In the same sense, Solar Pons is Sherlock Holmes. But while Sir Arthur Conan Doyle considerably updated Sherlock Holmes, I made little attempt to do so with Solar Pons, save only for a couple of decades or so. He remains for Pons a retired contemporary to whom Pons always refers as "the Master".

At the outset, I wrote to Sir Arthur to ask whether he intended to write more adventures of Sherlock Holmes. I waited for at least a year after publication of *The Casebook of Sherlock Holmes.* Early in autumn of 1928, when I was in my junior year at the University of Wisconsin, and holed up in a solitary back room at 823 West Johnson Street, Madison, Wisconsin (now the site of a rather impressive new dormitory), he replied—by means of a terse message scrawled upon my own letter—that he did not. He seemed, as I recall it now, unnecessarily emphatic about it, as if this decision, made once previously and set aside, were now irrevocable, and no amount of persuasion would this time cause him to change his mind. I wrote him that if he were not going to write further adventures, I would try my hand at it—but of course, this was impossible, for who was I to put upon paper new adventures of the illustrious Sherlock Holmes, of whom my maternal grandmother had always spoken as "the greatest detective who ever lived", since she, like so many other readers of the canon, was firmly convinced that Sherlock Holmes lived, not in that sense of the continuing life given him by the Baker Street Irregulars, but as an actual man of flesh and blood, who might be appealed to in cases of dire necessity.

The form the stories must take was patent. Not that ridiculing imitation designed for laughter, the parody, but that fond and admiring one less widely-known as the pastiche. I needed first a name, syllabically similar to that of Sherlock Holmes. So Solar Pons was born because I thought of Solar in its suggestion of light, and Pons as the bridge—"bridge of light" seemed to the adolescent mind singularly brilliant, which, of course, it was not.

Any other setting but England seemed out of the question. But in point of fact I knew very little about England, and even less about London. The England I knew and loved—having been all my life a pronounced Anglophile, despite an ancestry originally French, now largely Bavarian—was the England of Thomas Hardy, George Eliot, John Galsworthy, Jane Austen, Richard Jefferies, Gilbert White, Joseph Conrad, Mary Webb, W. H. Hudson—and the London that was the highly romantic and colorful city of Charles Dickens, Sir Arthur, Sax Rohmer, R. Austin Freeman and some other writers of detective and mystery fiction. This was admittedly neither much nor very accurate, insofar as even a tenuous reality for the Pontine tales was concerned.

Not long before beginning the first adventure of Solar Pons, I had read and enjoyed a novel by Cecil John Charles Street, under his pen-name of John Rhode, entitled *The Murders in Praed Street,* published in 1928, and when I cast around for the setting of the Pontine quarters, it was Praed Street that came instantly to mind. Perhaps my memory of the Dr. Priestley novel included some impressions of the milieu—that is, the naming of streets familiar to the canonical works, but of this I can no longer be certain. When I consulted Baedeker's *London and Its Environs*—which I had found necessary to buy, the first book on an expanding shelf that must now number close to two hundred books, ranging from street and provincial guides, to such comparatively recent works as A. J. P. Taylor's *English History: 1914-1945,* Eilert Ekwall's *The Concise Oxford Dictionary of English Place-Names,* Paul Ashbee's *The Bronze Age Round Barrow in Britain,* the Allen-Maxwell *The British Isles in Color,* and John Betjeman's *An American's Guide to English Parish Churches*—and learned that Praed Street was, for a hardy walker, actually within walking distance of 221B Baker Street, the Praed Street address seemed providential.

Thus Praed Street became the headquarters of Solar Pons,

and specifically number 7—for no reason but that this number came to mind and was set down, and number 7B, because Holmes was at 221B, though I then supposed that B indicated the second floor, when in fact, in London B designates the third floor—or what to American readers would be the third floor, since the first floor in London is that floor above the ground floor, which is the American first. I had no idea whatsoever about the actual and real Number 7, Praed Street, until late 1961, when Mr. Ian M. Law, who had visited Place of Hawks that summer, returned to England and considerately provided me with photographs of 7 Praed Street, which turned out to be next door to a cinema, and did have three floors, and could very readily have housed a private investigator and his amanuensis in their third floor quarters.

With the background fixed, however vaguely, in mind, I sat down and in one afternoon and evening wrote *The Adventure of the Black Narcissus*—my Baedeker's *London* at my elbow—which is precisely the kind of tale an amateur of nineteen would be likely to conjure up. Thereafter, this feat accomplished, the career of Solar Pons might have flatted and come to an unnoticed end, had it not been for a small circumstance. Harold Hersey, an indefatigable publisher, was at that time beginning a new string of pulp magazines in New York, and on impulse I sent the first Solar Pons story to him. Within a week came a check for $40.00, and—even more important, a letter saying that he would buy as many more Solar Pons stories as I cared to write for his magazine, *The Dragnet*.

With this promise of monetary reward added to what had already developed into a powerful compulsion, I went to work and in rapid succession, by dint of cutting classes here and there, I wrote *The Adventure of the Missing Tenants, The Adventure of the Broken Chessman,* and *The Adventure of the Late Mr. Faversham*. Harold Hersey bought them at once. In *The Adventure of the Black Narcissus* Solar Pons made his initial public appearance in the February, 1929 issue of *The Dragnet.* He appeared for the second time in the September issue of that year with *The Adventure of the Broken Chessman.*

I was now committed. In one day I turned out three pastiches—*The Adventure of the Viennese Musician, The Adventure of the Limping Man, The Adventure of Gresham Old Place*—and before the week was out, I had added *The Adventure of the Muttering Man, The Adventure of the Black Cardinal,* and *The Adventure of the Sotheby Salesman.* Two were immediately scheduled for publication, and the others accepted. And, counting my dollars to come in on publication, I went out to satisfy the most ardent of my desires—the acquisition of a library to supplement my shelves of Conan Doyle, Sax Rohmer, J. S. Fletcher, H. C. Bailey, Ernest Bramah, Lewis Carroll, Mark Twain and half a dozen other favorite authors. In one heady afternoon of buying, I acquired—on a charge account—$400 worth of books—by Proust, Dostoievsky, Tolstoi, Thomas Hardy, Turgenev, Robert Frost, Edgar Lee Masters, Sherwood Anderson, Sinclair Lewis, Andre Gide, Oscar Wilde—everything, in fact, I had wanted most badly—$400 worth, which I counted on Solar Pons to pay for. But alas!—the month was October, 1929—the market crash separated Harold Hersey and Solar Pons from *The Dragnet,* and, though Pons made three more appearances—in *Detective Trails* and *Gangster Stories,* in addition to *The Dragnet* in December, with *The Adventure of the Late Mr. Faversham*—his career had been effectively arrested.

I was left with $400 in debts and several returned manuscripts, as well as one new story of which I thought a trifle more favorably than I did its predecessors—*The Adventure of the Norcross Riddle.* Though I had learned so early in my career a valuable lesson every writer must learn sooner or later—not to count my chickens before the eggs were hatched!—Solar Pons was put on the shelf, while I went to work to complete studying for my B.A. in 1930, and then after graduation took an editorial post with Fawcett's, at that time in Minneapolis—the result of Donald Wandrei's recommendation after his rejection of the offer of that post. It was not congenial work, for all that my associates were pleasant and co-operative; I could not stick it much longer than four months and came home to do or die at writing, having managed in my short time as associate editor of *Mystic Magazine*—a short-lived Fawcett venture, to pay off my indebtedness, not alone at my editorial salary, but with the addition of payments for fiction and non-fiction turned out in my spare time.

I settled in at home and began to chronicle the saga of Sac Prairie, turning my inclinations toward detection into a series of book-length stories featuring Judge Ephraim Peabody Peck, who appeared in ten books and no more—*Murder Stalks the Wakely Family, The Man on All Fours, Three Who Died, Sign of Fear, Sentence Deferred, The Narracong Riddle, The Seven Who Waited, Mischief in the Lane, No Future for Luana,* and *Fell Purpose.* My regional fiction and poetry began to find berths in a gratifying variety of magazines ranging from little reviews like *This Quarter, The Midland,* and *Pagany,* to established magazines like *The Atlantic Monthly, The New Republic, Scribner's, Household, The Commonweal,* and many others; mystery novels were being followed into print by serious works like *Place of Hawks, Still Is the Summer Night, Wind Over Wisconsin,* et al., and I had been awarded a Guggenheim Fellowship to carry on the Sac Prairie Saga. As the years went by, Solar Pons was all but forgotten, but, truth to tell, Solar Pons had always had more reality in my thoughts than Judge Peck, for all that the estimable Judge operated in a milieu I knew very well indeed.

Yet Solar Pons might have been forgotten, had it not been for another fortuitous circumstance. Over a decade after the last—and I thought final appearance of Solar Pons (in *Gangster*

Stories for March, 1930, in *The Adventure of the Black Cardinal*)—Ellery Queen began to assemble stories for his anthology, *The Misadventures of Sherlock Holmes* (1944). I remembered *The Adventure of the Norcross Riddle* and wrote to Fred Dannay, asking whether he would like to see the pastiche. He welcomed it. So I undertook a retouching and retyping and sent it in. He accepted and published it; Irregulars read it with pleasure. Both Dannay and Vincent Starrett inquired about Solar Pons and, learning that there were enough tales for a group, urged that they be put out in book form.

Even so, I was far from convinced. I looked them all over; they seemed to me very amateurish indeed. None ranked with the single story published in the *Misadventures,* and I quietly resolved to let the idea of a Solar Pons collection die. Quite by chance, however, while discussing with Ray Palmer, then with Ziff-Davis in Chicago, the idea of a horror story anthology (later successfully published by Rinehart as *Sleep No More!*), I mentioned the possibility of a Solar Pons collection. Palmer urged me to put it together and, without committing Ziff-Davis to it, asked to see such a book with a view to publication.

With that added incentive and the promise from Vincent Starrett to write an introduction to the book, I went home and got to work to assemble a collection to be titled *"In Re: Sherlock Holmes": The Adventures of Solar Pons*—because, on the day I had decided to write a Holmesian pastiche, I had opened my desk calendar at 823 West Johnson at random and written "In re: Sherlock Holmes" to remind myself to write the story on that day, which I did. But when I re-examined those early stories—published and unpublished—there were then an even dozen—I found most of them simply too inept to be published. So I got to work and wrote new stories, while revising the old.

I kept *The Adventure of the Black Narcissus, The Adventure of the Norcross Riddle, The Adventure of the Sotheby Salesman, The Adventure of the Limping Man,* and *The Adventure of the Late Mr. Faversham.* The new tales were *The Adventure of the Man with the Broken Face, The Adventure of the Frightened Baronet, The Adventure of the Purloined Periapt, The Adventure of the Lost Holiday, The Adventure of the Three Red Dwarfs, The Adventure of the Retired Novelist* and *The Adventure of the Seven Passengers.* These stories made up the first collection, which was duly submitted to Ziff-Davis, and presently rejected.

By this time, however, I was infected with the virus. I was no longer so willing to trust any publisher with Solar Pons and, since I already had a publishing venture of my own in Arkham House—begun in 1939, six years earlier—I took especial pleasure in establishing a new imprint—Mycroft & Moran, the directors of which were, of course, Mycroft Holmes and Colonel Seabastian Moran ("the second most dangerous man in London")—in fixing upon Baskerville type for the Pontine tales, and commissioning a deerstalker as a colophon from Ronald Clyne, who had lent his artistry to the improvement of jackets for Arkham House books—and in 1945 Solar Pons made his bow in book form in the first collection, a full-length pastiche of *The Adventures of Sherlock Holmes.*

The Sources of the Tales

WITHOUT exception, the Solar Pons stories have been written around titles. None of the stories was ever conceived without the prior challenge of the title. Curiously enough, no plot ever challenged me as much as a title. Sometimes the title comes straight out of the canon—*The Adventure of the Remarkable Worm, The Adventure of the Late Mr. Faversham, The Adventure of Ricoletti of the Club Foot, The Adventure of the Grice-Paterson Curse, The Adventure of the Trained Cormorant, The Adventure of the Red Leech.* This last-named title had challenged me for some years, and it was not until I looked up leeches in the Encyclopaedia Britannica and discovered that there was actually, like the remarkable worm, no such thing as a red leech, that the story worked itself out.

Sometimes—perhaps in the majority of cases—a title is purely imaginary, a title occurring to me because I liked the sound or the promise of it, and teasing me until I have brought into existence a story to fit it, though, alas! I am forced to conclude far too often that the story does not measure up to the promise of the title. On occasion, a title is chanced upon in something seen or read, like *The Adventure of the Whispering Knights* and *The Adventure of the Mosaic Cylinders,* both of which grew out of letters published in *Country Life,* one of several British magazines to which I subscribe.

Under the heading of *Midland Stonehenge,* one "M. W." of Hereford wrote concerning the Rollright Stones on the boundary of Oxfordshire and Warwickshire. His letter was accompanied by a photograph of this Bronze Age stone circle, which instantly appealed to my imagination. In the final paragraph of the letter occurred this line: "About 100 yards east of the circle is a large Megalithic burial chamber, called the Whispering Knights . . ." Then and there the title was born, and it went into its gestation period for a shorter time—only a month—than usual. It took precedence over another title, *The Adventure of the Ritual Survival,* tucked away in mind after reading of a presumably ritual murder set forth in E. Spencer Shew's *Second Companion to Murder. I* combined the two, discarded the earlier title, and wrote *The Adventure of the Whispering Knights.*

Lest it be thought that this writing came wholly out of my imagination, I should point out that, in addition to the letter in *Country Life* and Shew's admirable *Companion,* I had to draw upon these books for the story's background—*The ABC Railway Guide,* Baedeker's *Great Britain* (1927 edition), George Long's *The Folklore Calendar,* Lewis Spence's *The History and Origins of Druidism,* Violet Alford's *Introduction to English Folklore,* Sydney R. Jones's *England West,* Robert Munro's *Prehistoric Britain,* and the *Britannica.* Every story in the Pontine canon has required more or less books for what I hope is the authenticity of its background. The writing of the first Pontine novel, *Mr. Fairlie's Final Journey,* for instance, required descriptive guides—some of the *Little Red Guides,* supplied by G. Ken Chapman—of areas around Frome, Somerset, Scotland, and Wales—and application to Chapman and Michael Harrison for specific details of idiom.

The Adventure of the Mosaic Cylinders was suggested by another letter in *Country Life,* in the issue for June 26, 1958, accompanied by an illustration of a sovereign box, designed as a puzzle box, locked by a cipher—very much as that described in that story. *The Adventure of the China Cottage* took rise virtually over night from a lavishly-illustrated article in *Country Life* for December 5, 1963—*Cottages to Scent a Room,* by G.

Bernard Hughes. I have in my files at least a dozen letters or random paragraphs clipped from this fine magazine from any or all of which future pastiches may grow.

Now and then, too, real life has afforded me an adventure for the series. Any reader interested enough to look into *Bernard Spilsbury: His Life and Cases,* by Douglas G. Browne and E. V. Tullett (George G. Harrap & Company, Ltd., 1951) will discover the source of *The Adventure of the Cloverdale Kennels* in the account of the unsolved Coverdale Kennels shootings, on pages 351-355, and the source of *The Adventure of the "Triple Kent"* in an account of the murder of Mrs. Dorothy Fisher, her daughter, and Miss Charlotte Saunders in the village of Matfield, Kent, in 1940, on pages 349-351. The former story in the series is wholly imaginary, for all that it has its source in the Spilsbury biography, while the latter incorporated some of the facts of the tragedy in the fiction. It is not a coincidence that the name "Spilsbury" occurs now and then in the pastiches.

The challenge of an unsolved mystery is always provocative —the Coverdale Kennels crime is one such, and the almost legendary account of strange footprints in the snow discovered February 1, 1855 in Devonshire—footprints that resembled some very large hoofed creature, all in a line that led through seventeen towns for a distance of approximately a hundred miles, leading along roads, through woods, fields, and gardens, across streams and farmhouse roofs alike, and made without any sound to alert the natives, is another. The mystery of the footprints was never solved, but the tale gave rise to *The Adventure of the Devil's Footprints,* just as the account of the famous Lost Dutchman mine in the American Southwest—a tale integral to the legendry and lore of the Southwest—brought into being *The Adventure of the Lost Dutchman.*

Just as I go about constantly in the microcosm of Sac Prairie alert for aspects of life to chronicle, I am always alert for an idea or a plot that will lend itself to a Pontine pastiche. It may be an incident—a newspaper account of an unsolved murder—*The Adventure of the Sotheby Salesman,* for example, took rise from a brief account of the discovery of a murdered man thought to be a tramp in an empty house—a chance remark, an historical trifle—*The Adventure of the Rydberg Numbers* had its inception in the scientific inquiries into the possibilities of atomic fission that went on in the 1920s both in England and on the Continent—an event in the news—*The Adventure of the Stone of Scone* roughly follows the events of the actual theft of the stone from Westminster some years ago.

On occasion, nothing more than a whim gives motivation for a story. *The Adventure of the Penny Magenta* was written simply because I wanted to write a pastiche with a philatelic background; *The Adventure of the Mazarine Blue* because I took a fancy to the name of that butterfly (ironically, the editor of the magazine that published it, retitled it *The Thirteenth Coffin*). Sometimes, too, I am taken up by what someone has written. While convalescing in the hospital some years ago I read Ivor Brown's *A Word in Your Ear* and *Just Another Word,* and I was so enchanted by the lost words in the language that I evolved *The Adventure of the Amateur Philologist.* Similarly, that magnificent book, *Tutankhamen,* by Christiane Desroches-Noblecourt, suggested *The Adventure of the Crouching Dog* in its reproduction of the seal on the tomb of the Pharaoh.

On the other hand, at least one story grew out of a dream. I dreamed one night that I was secreted somewhere in a copse or grove in the dusk, and from this hiding-place saw a man, surrounded by six mastiffs, running through the twilight without a sound other than that made by their steps; within hours of waking from that dream, I had evolved *The Adventure of the Sussex Archers,* into which I incorporated the events of the dream.

An announcement from the Folio Society of London about the Society's forthcoming publication of *Dickens' London* was the inception for *The Adventure of the Unique Dickensians.* The Society's book was a collection of the essays Dickens had written about the city, to illustrate which the announcement reprinted not only some of the old Cruikshank illustrations but also some of the London street cries of the period—for example, *Cherries:*

> Round and sound
> Twopence a pound
> Cherries, rare ripe cherries!
> Cherries a ha'penny a stick
> Come and pick! Come and pick!
> Cherries big as plums!
> Who comes, who comes?

These caught my fancy, and, given a natural predilection for Dickens, the sort of double pastiche that became *The Adventure of the Unique Dickensians* was born, and set down in the space of seven hours (over a period of four days) immediately after completion of *Mr. Fairlie's Final Journey* early in 1968.

There are in my Pontine files newspaper clippings without number which have caught my eye suggestively; at any time a pastiche may grow from one of them. Their headings range widely—as I hope for the pastiches to range—*Timber Scribing* (another letter in *Country Life*)—*A Memory of Exmoor—Britain's Great Train Robbery—Last Days of a Gothic Masterpiece—Christmas at Caldermoor—Grouse Hawking in Caithness—Rothern Bridge Doomed—Is Clophill Magic as Black as It's Been Painted?—The Haunted Hills of Wales—The Great Portuguese Banknote Swindle—Letters of Guilt—Patterns of Murder—Brown Windsor for Dr. Johnson—Stock Exchange Under Fire—Nightjars on a Southern Common—The Varied Fortunes of a Derbyshire Spa—Witches and Wizards of the Fens.*

Some titles persistently resist explication. *The Adventure of*

Cagliostro Second, for example. Perhaps a new biography of *Cagliostro,* on my desk as I write, may provide me with a lead. Or *The Adventure of the Pope's Guardsman*—I am reluctant to move Pons to Rome, and what would a member of the Swiss Guard be about in London?—certainly not his business. Or *The Adventure of the Lost Metternich* and *The Adventure of the Italian Letters*—perhaps these resist me because there are other tales pressing more urgently to be written—like *The Adventure of Mr. Peppercorn's Folly* or *The Adventure of the Aluminum Crutch* or the tantalizing *Adventure of the Sussex Beekeeper.*

I suspect there are always more suggested plots and themes—and more titles for new stories—than I will be able to write before the basic repetitiousness of the pattern intervenes to end the series—or I myself shuffle off this mortal coil.

Concerning Dr. Parker's Background

MR. CHARLES H. WAREING of Birmingham, England, a solicitor by profession and a Pons enthusiast by inclination, was appalled on reading *The Adventure of the Black Narcissus,* to discover how very un-English Dr. Parker was, and subsequently Michael Harrison, the distinguished author of many books—among them several pertinent to the London of Sherlock Holmes and associated subjects—pointed out, after beginning an acquaintance with Solar Pons, that Dr. Parker wrote prose that could best be described as "semi-American".

I was not unduly surprised to learn of their reactions, for, truth to tell, that fellow Parker has had some dark antecedents, and seems to have come upon the scene by fortuitous happenstance. "I had been sitting for some time in a pub not far from Paddington Station, ruefully reflecting that the London to which I had returned after the first World War was not the city I had left," he writes of himself, "when a tall, thin gentleman wearing an Inverness cape and a rakish cap with a visor on it, strode casually into the place." This is certainly ambiguous, to say the least.

There is nothing about his antecedents; he mentions the London to which he "returned" after the war, and we are told that he "left" London, but nothing is said as to when he left it, and Michael Harrison has suggested that there must be "a good reason for" Parker's writing "in a style full of Americanisms." Dark hints, these. There is evidently some chapter in Parker's life that will bear examination and revelation, and perhaps in it we shall find an explanation for his peculiar prose, which is neither really British nor fully American, and is adequate proof that, as Harrison puts it, it is hardly "possible for a writer trained in one idiom to write, even as a careful exercise, in another," a premise I cannot dispute.

Harrison has suggested bluntly that Parker must have spent some of the years before the war—perhaps as a youth—in the United States and, indefatigable explorer of past times that he is, has promised to investigate those earlier years. A pity I had not done so myself. Of course, it is now too late. Being a writer trained in the American idiom myself and hence peculiarly blind to the flaws in Dr. Parker's prose, I am at this point far too apprehensive about what I might turn up to dig back a little into his antecedents. It should have been done before this.

It is all very well to say, as Harrison does, "you can now say anything you like about him," but can I? I doubt it. Here he is now, as I conceived him, a stolid, middle-class, rather unimaginative Englishman, not without a certain wit and loyal attachment—to Pons particularly, and to England generally—and it is altogether too unsettling to think that this may be simply front —a protective covering, as it were, intended to deceive me, of all people, and, of course, through me, an ever-growing host of others who are, like me, prepared to take him at face value.

Perhaps there is indeed a good reason for Parker's rather consistent self-effacement in the little chronicles about his friend, Solar Pons. I had not noticed this, either, until the persistence of Michael Harrison brought it to my attention. Parker does not bring himself into the adventures any more than need be. And when he does so in his own *Notebooks* it is only because Pons draws information out of him, as in the entry for 28 September 1919; even here he chronicles his replies to Pons's queries "reluctantly", and "somewhat stiffly". I had thought this only proper for him in the role he played—as an observer, in most cases, of his companion's skill at deduction and detection, but his motive may have been quite otherwise. There are certain disquieting references in Dr. Parker's *Notebooks,* not all of which have seen the light of day.

I think it best, after all, to leave this entire subject to other, more impartial hands.

The Favorite Pastiches

IT IS NO SECRET that Sir Arthur Conan Doyle looked upon the Sherlock Holmes tales with a highly critical—and sometimes a jaundiced eye, a point-of-view which readers have always found difficult to understand, but which any other writer of series stories understands only too well. The repetition of devices, gambits, situations tells considerably more on the patience of the author than on that of the reader, and helps to accentuate the shortcomings of the individual stories in any series.

It should therefore be not surprising to learn that only two of the pastiches satisfy their author—*The Adventure of the Purloined Periapt* and *The Adventure of the Six Silver Spiders*—and that only perhaps a dozen others seem to me of merit. It is also the fixed conviction of the author that Solar Pons is at his best in the shorter form, and that the deductive detective of this stamp functions at somewhat of a disadvantage in the form of the novel.

Editorial and reader perspectives sometimes differ, however, and I have found it interesting to take note of these differences. Frederic Dannay manifestly prefers *The Adventure of the Six Silver Spiders* over all the other Pontine tales; it alone saw publication in *Ellery Queen's Mystery Magazine;* Anthony Boucher shares the author's preference for *The Adventure of the Purloined Periapt;* and Vincent Starrett has always preferred *The Adventure of the Late Mr. Faversham*—perhaps because it takes rise in one of the unwritten tales of Watson—with Dannay's first choice coming in second. "But I have never failed to read a Solar Pons adventure with satisfaction and pleasure," he writes.

Luther Norris, who prepared the *London Map of Solar Pons* and inaugurated the Praed Street Irregulars, sets down as his prime favorite *The Adventure of the Norcross Riddle,* one of the earliest of the tales; "Here is the tradition of deduction at its very best," according to him. Following this one on Norris's list comes Starrett's favorite, *The Adventure of the Late Mr. Faversham,* and then, in order, *The Adventure of the Black Narcissus, The Adventure of the Six Silver Spiders, The Adventure of the Camberwell Beauty* ("the double pastiche is a pure delight!"), *The Adventure of the Rydberg Numbers, The Adventure of the Frightened Baronet, The Adventure of the Penny Magenta* ("A nostalgic reminder of London and Baker Street days."), *The Adventure of the Purloined Periapt* and *The Adventure of the Intarsia Box.*

Peter Ruber selects, without placing them in any order, *The Adventure of the Mosaic Cylinders, The Adventure of the Purloined Periapt, The Adventure of the Circular Room, The Adventure of the Six Silver Spiders, The Adventure of the Rydberg Numbers, The Adventure of the Norcross Riddle, The Adventure of the Lost Holiday, The Adventure of the Broken Chessman, The Adventure of the Swedenborg Signatures, The Adventure of the Magazine Blue,* and *The Adventure of the Orient Express.* "I should probably substitute other titles if I were to sit down and reread all the stories," writes Ruber, "but, as in the Holmes series, my favorites number only six or seven: it is the whole series that is important."

Robert Bloch's esteem, too, "extends to the entire canon." He adds, perceptively, "Aside from the personal pleasure I derive from reading any dispatch from Praed Street, there is another dimension that delights me. Specifically, I think of a small boy in a midwestern farm community—a small boy curled in a chair before the glowing coal stove on a bleak winter evening and devouring with wide-eyed wonder the exploits of Sherlock Holmes in the London of far away and long ago. I think of that boy grown to manhood and creating his own colorful criminologist and his own legendary London—and thus adding to the enjoyment of all of us who remember, as he does, the enchantment that commences when the game is afoot. In a word, I cannot dissociate the exploits of Solar Pons from the exploits of his Agent—and I'm grateful for them both."

Poul Anderson finds it as difficult as the majority of readers to select one Solar Pons story as *the* favorite. "They are all such delightful pastiches, and good yarns in their own right. So if *The Adventure of the Ball of Nostradamus* stands out especially in my mind, it is because of another element—the fantasy, the deft use of the paradoxes inherent in prediction. Yet the story is more than a brief entertainment. It raises a moral issue which lies at the very foundations of real-world politics and much other human action. Think about it."

Joseph Payne Brennan, himself the author of a sleuthing series, chooses as his three favorites *The Adventure of the Grice-Paterson Curse, The Adventure of the Late Mr. Faversham,* and *The Adventure of the Crouching Dog*. He points out that "stories quite often appeal for quite personal, rather than literary, reasons. I like the atmosphere of brooding horror hanging over that mysterious island of Uffa in *The Adventure of the Grice-Paterson Curse*. . . . Mr. Faversham came close to committing the really classic crime! He might have been a really great criminal—cut from the same cloth as the great Moriarty! (By what mischance we miss enduring fame!) And I suppose *The Adventure of the Crouching Dog* appeals to me strongly because I am carried back in reminiscence to the great days of the immortal *Hound*. The brooding moor, the great paw prints, the curse—all are there, all the lovely lethal ingredients! Apart from the supernatural, what can rival a mysterious canine killer bounding across a darkened moor toward its terrified victim?"

A personal inclination decided A. E. Van Vogt's choice of favorite story—*The Adventure of the Mazarine Blue.* "Over the years I have occasionally read a story in which an insect is utilized as a major factor. The very first time I was impressed by the astuteness of the author in conceiving such a plot, and it seemed to me that, surely, it could be done only once or twice with effectiveness in the whole of literature. When Derleth did it—again—in *The Adventure of the Mazarine Blue,* I felt an admiration not diminished by any other of the pastiches."

A wide variety of selections come from many sources, but it is nevertheless evident that the author's two prime favorites are mentioned frequently enough to suggest that the principal criterion of judgment would appear to be similarity to the Holmesian canon, and by this standard, *The Adventure of the Purloined Periapt* and *The Adventure of the Six Silver Spiders* are the most Holmesian of the pastiches thus far written.

Yet the odds-on favorite deductive passage does not appear in either of these stories. An overwhelming majority of Pontine devotees have chosen as their best-liked deductive passage the opening paragraphs of *The Adventure of the Norcross Riddle,* following upon Pons's invitation to Parker to address his "intuition" to a calling card. The passage follows—

The card bore an embossed legend: "Mr. Benjamin Harrison Manton," and in one corner, in smaller print, "Norcross Towers." I turned it over. The caller had written on its back, *Will call at three.*

"My observation tells me that the gentleman used a broad-point pen; the character of the writing indicates that he is firm and steady. I see he uses the Roman *e* consistently; my intuition tells me he is an intelligent man."

Pons's smile widened, and he chuckled again.

"What do *you* make of it?" I asked, somewhat nettled.

"Oh, little more," replied Pons matter-of-factly, "except that the gentleman is an American by birth, but has resided in England for some length of time; he is a man of independent means, and is between thirty-five and thirty-nine years of age. Furthermore, his ancestry is very probably Southern United States, but his parents were undoubtedly members of the American Republican political party."

"You have seen the man!"

"Nonsense!" Pons picked up the card. "Observe:—the name *Manton* is more common to the southern part of the United States than to any other region; undoubtedly it is English in ancestry. In that part of the States, political sentiment is very largely Democratic, but it is not amiss to suggest that Manton's parents were Republican in sentiment, since they named him after a Republican president."

"Well, that is simple," I admitted.

"Precisely, Parker. But there is no intuition about it. It is mere observation. Now test yourself—tell me how I know he is of independent means."

"He calls at three," I ventured. "Certainly if he were not of independent means he could not break into an afternoon like that."

"He might well get away from his work to visit us," objected Pons. "Examine the card more closely."

"Well, it is embossed; that is a more expensive process than simple printing."

"Good, Parker. Come, you are getting there!"

"And the card itself is of very fine quality, though not pretentious." I held it up against the window. "Imported paper, I see. Italian."

"Excellent!"

"But how do you know he has lived in England for some time?"

"That is the most elementary of all. The gentleman has purchased or rented a country place, possibly an abandoned English home, for 'Norcross Towers' is certainly the name of a country house."

"But his age!" I protested. "How can you know the man's age merely by glancing at his calling card?"

"That is really absurdly simple, Parker. In the States it is considered fashionable even today to name children after the president in office at the time of the child's birth; doubtless the American tendency to hero-worship plays its part in that, too. Harrison was president from 1889 to 1893; hence it follows that our man was born in one of the four years of Harrison's term. The age is more likely to be thirty-nine years, because the tendency to name children in such fashion is strongest during the inaugural period."

I threw up my hands. "The contest is yours!"

A propos favorites, my daughter April Rose, at ten years of age settled that matter decisively. I put out for her one day two stories to read—*The Adventure of the Speckled Band* from the Master Canon, and *The Adventure of the Lost Locomotive* from the Pontine pastiches. She read them both with interest and declared that she liked them equally well. I observed, however, that it was to Sherlock Holmes that she returned, and not to Solar Pons.

From the Notebooks of Dr. Lyndon Parker

WITHIN A FEW months of my joining Solar Pons in his quarters at 7B, Praed Street, and before I turned to chronicling his cases at full-length, I began to keep a notebook—not one of daily accounting, but only of random jottings, having become interested enough in his methods to seek to preserve some of his feats. For, in addition to adventures I later set down, there were many instructive moments in his company, and many lesser problems that came and went, that I wished to set down in some fashion for my own edification, and, later, to refresh my memory, since the memory of man is fallible, and time diminishes it or distorts what is locked in it. The entries that follow all date back to my first year at 7B.

17 August 1919

After a brief lecture on the art of observation and deduction in a pub in Camden Town today, Pons singled out a disgruntled-looking young man of not over thirty sitting by himself and put me to the test.

"What do you make of him, Parker?"

"A laborer," I said.

"Too general," retorted Pons.

"He is upset and brooding about something. His face is morose, he hardly touches his ale."

"Capital!" cried Pons. "Go on."

"He seems to be engaged in some sort of manual labor. His hands are rough."

Pons looked at me keenly, his eyes twinkling. "Nothing more?"

"Except that he seems to have come away hastily. He is in his working clothes."

"Well, that is a good beginning," said Pons. "You have really missed only a few little details. Come, let us just go over and talk with him."

So saying, he rose and led the way to the corner where the object of our attention glowered into his ale. The fellow did not look up when we came to pause before him.

"Forgive me for interrupting your black mood," said Pons, "but perhaps your wife will come around and you can patch up your quarrel."

The fellow looked up, amazement spreading across his face. After a brief hesitation, he growled, "I'm done with that."

"Things are never as black as they seem," pursued Pons. "Perhaps by this time she has contemplated your wedding ring long enough to reflect on her position."

"It's the first time I took if off," he answered.

"You are by trade a mason?"

"Aye."

"Specifically, a brick-layer."

He nodded.

"Left-handed, I see."

The fellow now gazed at Pons with increasing bewilderment.

"Childless, too."

"Look here, I don't know your game . . ." The fellow pushed back his chair and would have got up, had not Pons dropped a coin to the table in front of him.

"Have another pint, young man," he said, and walked away.

Once outside, Pons explained the simplicity of it. "The fellow's dark mood coupled with the fact that the band of relatively clean skin on his ring finger betrayed the recent removal of what could only have been a wedding ring suggested that he and his wife had quarrelled. He would not be likely to take himself off so violently if there were children to consider.

"As for his calling—the fingertips of his right hand show the worn, shiny stigma of the brick-layer. Since the mason habitually lays bricks with his left hand while his right is busy with the trowel, it follows that our man is left-handed. Always, in scrutinizing anyone, look for the stigmata of his calling—if there be such. Observe, for instance, this slender young man approaching us. What do you make of the mark on his neck not far below his left ear?"

I looked as closely as I could at the area Pons designated, and identified it as an acneform dermatergosis.

"But what does it tell us?" asked Pons. "That is an area too high to be irritated by his collar."

I could not guess.

"Why, it is plain as a pikestaff that he plays either the violin or the viola, and I submit that it is the violin. The mark is characteristic of an irritation caused by holding that instrumet alongside the chin and against the neck."

28 September 1919

In our quarters today Pons surprised me by saying, "I have often reflected upon the fact that you have been somewhat less than comprehensive in your account of yourself to me, Parker."

"Why do you say so?" I asked.

"You have impressed me with the Order of Osmanieh bestowed upon you by the Khedivial Government as well as with His Majesty's Government's commission to continue the work at Mansura, Egypt. You have spoken of your education at Dover College, University College, and Heidelberg, and I have been privileged to read your series of articles on opthalmia in *The Lancet.* But you are curiously reticent about your years in America. Yet they must have been of some duration."

"Ten years," I said reluctantly.

"You have fallen rather pronouncedly into the American

idiom and I observe that you speak what can best be described as semi-American."

"I am not aware of it," I replied, I fear, somewhat stiffly.

"Oh, it is unmistakable," persisted Pons. "Let me illustrate. Only this morning you spoke of a shop's being 'on' Edgware Road, whereas we customarily say that it is 'in' this or that street. The American, however, usually says 'on'. You referred yesterday, in speaking of that unfortunate matter of the Curate's Mistake, to a 'stoop' when any Englishman would have said 'porch'. I cite but these two examples, of what I should say is an Englishman's speaking semi-American. You seem to have been spared some of the curious accents affected by Americans, however."

"Ah, that entire period is a painful one for me," I said.

"You did not enjoy your sojourn in the States?"

"No, it was not that. I was graduated from Columbia and then for two years, to 1903, I served as principal medical officer for the Allegheny Sheet & Tube Corporation. Those years were pleasant enough."

"Ah, it was your marriage."

"Say, rather, its unfortunate ending. Louisa's death in the *Titanic* disaster ended not only an entire period in my life, but a kind of life. The war followed hard upon it, and our world has changed since then. I have closed that door—Praed Street is as far from those American years as from my Egyptian sojourn."

With this he appeared to be satisfied, or, out of delicacy, said no more.

11 October 1919

Pons on Calluses,&c.—"Certain calluses are almost invariable. The stone-cutter, for instance, is likely to have a broad callus at the base of the little finger of his left hand, on the back, of course, where the chisel rests on the finger. A trumpet player—or a tuba player, for that matter—is likely to show a callus on the right little finger, whereas that of the French horn player will show on the left little finger. The jeweler or engraver may show calluses in several specific places, including the palm of the hand, the tips of thumb and index finger, particularly of the left hand.

"Men who work with coal tar and petroleum derivatives may show melanosis of exposed parts of their bodies, and anyone working with tetryl in any form is apt to show the red and yellow stains on skin and hair, whereas silversmiths tend to absorb enough silver to give a characteristic slate gray color to their skin.

"You will yourself be familiar with the stigmata of disease."

12 October 1919

I had been reading Pons's *The Varieties of the Criminal Method.* When I put the book down, I asked him whether there was such a thing as "the criminal type."

"I fear that is a fallacy," said Pons. "The fault for its existence is probably traceable to Lombroso, who held that there was such a thing."

"But you will admit that certain people look like criminals."

"Nonsense. They may perhaps fit the viewer's concept of what a criminal ought to look like, no more."

He got up and took down his files. From them he abstracted four photographs and laid them before me.

"Which of these is the criminal?" he asked.

"I suspect they are all criminals or you wouldn't have them in your files."

"On the contrary. Logical as your deduction is, your conclusion is false."

I examined the photographs carefully and finally selected one.

"Why?" asked Pons.

"You have only to look at him—the beetling brow, the shifty eyes, the thick-lipped sensuous mouth, the cauliflower ear. The fellow looks evil."

"And the others do not?"

"No."

"Why do you say so?"

"Well, look at the first one. There is an ascetic face, if ever I saw one," I said. "The fellow looks like a minister."

"He was. The Reverend Athelny Foster."

I fear I chuckled in triumph.

"Of Chipping Fulham. The name means nothing to you?"

"It is surely enough that I identified his calling."

"He poisoned his wife in favor of a barmaid," said Pons dryly. "Next?"

"This one is as dignified as a Sunday School Superintendent."

"You name him so?"

"No. A judge or a lawyer. And so is the other."

Pons laughed in that way of his I should describe as "heartless." "The one is a swindler of some renown—Patrick Donovan. The other is indeed a lawyer—Charles Convers. He suffocated a client in order to conceal his peculations from his estate."

"And what did the 'criminal type' do?"

"He caught them. He was the late Commissioner John Flinders of New Scotland Yard. I trust that will curb your romanticism."

17 October 1919

A lady called to see Pons today. She gave her name as Mrs. Rose Murray. She was simply dressed and wore a little straw hat with straw flowers decorating it, together with a bit of black cloth.

"A seamstress, I see," said Pons.

"Yes, sir," she said. "I didn't think it so plain to tell I made my own clothing."

"The mark of the thimble is easy to see on your finger," said Pons. "Not long widowed?"

"My husband was killed last March in an accident on the

Great Western," she replied. "I have quite got over it, though."

"Not quite enough to remove that bit of crepe on your hat, and yet enough to call yourself by your own Christian name rather than his."

"Yes, that is true."

"And what can I do for you, Mrs. Murray?"

"Why, Mr. Pons, I am an acquaintance of your landlady, and since you and Dr. Parker are bachelors, I took it you might have some sewing for me to do."

19 October 1919

Pons' persisting habits—

He toys with his ear, pulls at the lobe—usually his left, when in deep thought. (Freud would have something to say about this!) He also closes his eyes frequently to concentrate the better.

He is an attentive listener. Sitting, he tends to tent his fingers. Standing, he leans against the mantel most frequently. On occasion he paces back and forth, hands clasped behind him.

His eyes seem alternately grey or grey-green. They seem to be extraordinarily keen and alive. He seems to miss nothing. His glance is quick—"darting" would be the word, and he seems to look into one.

He smokes the most abominable shag ever prepared by the hand of man. I could believe it to be a mixture of cabbage leaves, string, and the Chinese tea smoked from the burning of yak dung. He keeps it wherever the fancy suits him—the coal scuttle, the toe of a slipper, the pen cup, etc.

He delights to display his deductive powers, but at the same time he vastly appreciates it when the joke is on him.

His is devoted to his Inverness and deerstalker, but I wonder sometimes if he does not wear them for effect only. (If that is blasphemy—*mea culpa.*) He has dressing-gowns in several colors, all dark—and all well worn. He shows no inclination to get himself a new robe.

He is much given to disguising himself. He fancies, because he has deceived me so readily several times, that he is very good at disguise, forgetting that, as he has pointed out on even more occasions, I am not as observant as I ought to be.

7 November 1919

Inspector Jamison called today to lay a problem before Pons. He was apologetic about its trivial nature—repeated house-breaking in Park Lane—but it was evident that he was vexed about it, nevertheless. He gave an account of seven break-ins all within two blocks, and ended finally with, "The crux of the matter, Pons, is its senselessness."

"I daresay its meaning has not yet become evident," said Pons dryly.

"Every one a clumsy break-in, and nothing of value taken."

"An amateur's work, clearly?"

"No doubt of it."

"Or made to seem so. Let me see, now," Pons went on, leaning back in his chair at the fireplace, his eyes closed, his fingers tented before him. "A Chinese piece stolen at the Forrer home?"

"Value about one pound," said Jamison.

"Nothing more?"

"Nothing. One item from each house."

"A gold-plated pen from the Beston house."

Jamison shrugged. "Ten shillings—if that. It wasn't the loss Beston reported so much as the breakage—a pane of the back door broken in while they were gone."

"In all cases the householders were absent," mused Pons. "So the burglar seemed to have some knowledge of their movements."

"Yes, yes, Pons—all that is elementary," said Jamison impatiently. "What good did it do him to watch these houses if all he meant to take was some trifling article? That's the work of an imbecile."

"I would not say so," said Pons. "The most expensive item taken appears to have been a cheap brooch from the Kendall home," he went on.

"Under two pounds value," said Jamison.

"And entry, if I understood you, seems to have been made in every case before midnight."

"In two cases before ten-thirty o'clock. The householders got home by ten-thirty."

Pons smiled. "This suggests nothing to you, Jamison?"

"The man's a fool. Or he means to be a nuisance. Perhaps he wants to put the wind up somebody in that neighborhood."

"I submit it is more than that," said Pons with an annoying habit, which I had observed before, of saying too little.

"I suppose next you will be telling me to look for a short fat man with a limp, who smokes nothing but imported cigars and is supporting his mother-in-law," said Jamison with heavy sarcasm.

Pons laughed heartily. "I regret I cannot oblige you this time, Jamison. I think the honor of catching him must be yours. But then," he added, his eyes dancing, "it always has been, has it not?"

"You *can* describe him then?" asked Jamison, incredulous.

"I do not know whether he is short or tall, fat or lean," said Pons, "and at this point, I am sorry to say, the case does not seem to me interesting enough to challenge me. And, if I may say so, it is too elementary."

Jamison got to his feet as abruptly as his bulk permitted. "I shall have to look elsewhere."

"I suggest you sit tight and let him betray himself."

"Ah, and how many times will he have to do a burglarious entry before then?"

"I rather think he has done almost as many as he needs to do," continued Pons. "At any time now he will make a mistake."

Jamison's interest quickened. "What sort of mistake?"

"He will steal something of value. Perhaps of great value. And something certain to be heavily insured. You will then, of course, investigate thoroughly the financial situation of the gentleman who reports the theft. I submit you will find that all the other burglaries were performed only to make his own loss credible. I can foresee the headlines: *Inspector Jamison Scores Again!*"

"And if nothing of the sort happens?" asked Jamison skeptically.

"Then by all means call on me again and I will be happy to look into the matter."

18 November 1919

At my place at breakfast this morning, Pons, who had gone out, had left the morning paper with a small item circled in red crayon. "Inspector Jamison Scores," I read. "Mr. Geoffrey Thompson was taken into custody this morning and charged with a series of burglaries in Park Lane. Mr. Thompson had only two days ago reported himself as the victim of such a burglary, having lost a valuable pearl necklace belonging to his wife . . ." No mention of Pons, of course; but that is how he prefers it.

21 November 1919

A short man, introducing himself as Mr. Howard Robinson, retired, came to see Pons this morning. He was not over five feet in height, and thin almost to cadaverousness. His bearing was military. A moustache he wore would on almost anyone else have looked fierce, but on him had the appearance of something attached for effect. He had rough hands.

"I have, Mr. Pons, a rather delicate problem." I observed that he pronounced "ra-ther" in two distinct and separate syllables. "Late yesterday I received a sealed envelope in which my solicitor forwarded to me a certain legacy in bank-notes. While the covering letter was enclosed, the bank-notes were not. Yet the seal was unboken. My solicitor is a man of the utmost honesty, so that one of the three persons through whose hands this envelope passed from him to me must have taken the banknotes. But how? I looked in on Thornydke, but he was in Scotland. I took the liberty of coming to you without an appointment.

All prim and proper, and very businesslike.

"You have the envelope, Mr. Robinson?" asked Pons.

"Yes, sir."

Robinson produced it, carefully wrapped in gauze, from a pocket case of hard leather. He handed it to Pons.

"I see by its shape that it certainly did at one time contain something of bulk," said Pons at once.

"I thought so. I opened it with an opener. The letter, you see, has plainly been wrapped around something—certainly the bank-notes."

"Let us just see." So saying, Pons carried the envelope over to the corner of our quarters where he amused himself with chemicals. He sat down there, took up his magnifying glass, and studied the seal. I heard him chuckle. "Pray step over here, Mr. Robinson."

Robinson did so. I was at his heels.

"See there, sir," said Pons, pointing to a mere speck of grey on the maroon wax of the seal. "This is plaster of Paris. Someone took off the seal and replaced it."

"But how, sir?"

Pons leaned back. "Why, by a common method indeed. Someone oiled the seal and poured on to it some freshly burned plaster of Paris. As soon as it was set, the seal was raised. After the money was taken out of the envelope, the seal was renewed from the oiled mould. It is almost inevitable that flakes or grains of the plaster will stick to the seal. There is evidence here that some grains were removed."

"It will hold up in court?"

"Any competent witness can testify to it successfully."

"Would you be willing to do so?"

"If I am called upon, Mr. Robinson. If I am called upon," said Pons. He stood up so suddenly that Mr. Robinson fell back. "That will be two pounds, sir."

"Two—two pounds?" stuttered Robinson.

"Two pounds," said Pons with such finality that Robinson paid him forthwith.

He bowed himself out.

Pons threw the notes to the table and walked over to the window to watch our late client emerge from 7B.

"Nature provides an infinite variety in mankind," he reflected. "What did you make of him, Parker?"

"An ex-military man," I said at once.

"Capital!" said Pons. "But obvious. It has been a long time since he was in military service."

"And a man accustomed to clerical work."

"Ah, you make progress. You saw the typical middle-finger callus of a man who has used a pen for a long time. Nothing more?"

"I did think his clothes a trifle old."

"Excellent. And worn. The fellow is a miser. You saw how taken aback he was when I asked a fee."

"I did indeed."

"I submit, moreover, that he is very probably also a potential thief. There was plaster of Paris also under one of his fingernails. He came here to test his plan. Greed has made a bungler of him. He ought never to have opened the envelope save in the presence of witnesses. We shall hear no more from him."

26 November 1919

Our landlady, Mrs. Johnson, tapped rather timidly at our door today. When I had opened to her, she excused herself, apologized for her temerity, and addressed herself to Pons.

"Mr. Pons, sir, I wonder it it would be too much if I asked Lillie Morris up to talk to you. What with the new will they found, she's that upset and all."

"What is her trouble, Mrs. Johnson?"

"Why, it's the new will," she said, as if he might have known. "The old will gave everything to her—and the new one nothing. And after she took care of the old man, too!"

"Pray ask her up, Mrs. Johnson," said Pons, his eyes twinkling.

I could not help saying, after our landlady had gone down to her quarters, "More than once, I've had that particular failing called to mind—some woman who gives a decade or more of her life to taking care of an aged father or mother or other relative is done out of her rightful due by another member of the family who shows up from time to time and who sends around little gifts now and then. Old people exaggerate the little differences that invariably develop between them and those who care for them, and fail to realize that it is quite the easiest thing to do them an occasional kindness without the day to day exchange arising to sully the impression so easily created."

Pons nodded. "That is only another trifle of evidence in support of human frailty."

"Do you know Mrs. Johnson's friend?"

"I have never heard of her before."

Mrs. Johnson presently appeared with Lillie Morris in tow. She was a woman in her early thirties not ill-favored in looks, with brown eyes at present a bit clouded with trouble. She was neatly but not expensively dressed, and wore her ash-blonde hair attractively piled on to her head. Since she wore no wedding band, I concluded that she was unmarried.

"Pray sit down, Miss Morris, and tell me your trouble," invited Pons.

Miss Morris had brought up her reticule, and this she now put beside the chair on which she sat. Mrs. Johnson took a seat between her friend and the door, and sat leaning forward expectantly, as if at any moment a miracle might be produced by my companion to ease her friend's mind.

"Thank you, Mr. Pons." And what a pleasant, well-modulated voice she had! "Mrs. Johnson said you would be kind enough to listen to me, though I'm sure I am imposing upon you. For the past eleven years I have had my living with my grandfather who needed someone to take care of him, and when he died, he left a will leaving his house and what he owned to me."

"A considerable sum or a modest one?" interposed Pons.

"I believe it is considerable, Mr. Pons. But it seems I am not to get it after all. A later will has turned up, and he has left it all to my cousin Percy, with whom he was on friendly terms."

"Percy lived with him?"

"Oh, no, Mr. Pons. Percy lives in Soho. But he came around now and then and took grandfather out for a day. Mrs. Johnson says I ought to contest the will, and so do some of my other friends."

"You have seen the will, Miss Morris?"

"I was sent a photographic copy of it."

"Ah. Pray let me see it."

Miss Morris took a fat envelope from her reticule and from this took the document in question and passed it to Pons.

He unfolded it and glanced at it. His eyes narrowed. "Why, it is dated less than a half a year ago," he said.

"My grandfather died two months past," said Miss Morris.

Pons read rapidly through the will. "Each page separately signed, I see."

"Yes, Mr. Pons. I am afraid there is no doubt it is my grandfather's signature. No doubt at all. Even I would have to testify to it."

Pons' eyes, I saw, grew intent as he looked at first one page and then another, until he had finished the fourth page. He lowered the will but continued to hold on to it while he gazed thoughtfully at Miss Morris.

"How old was your grandfather when he died?" he asked.

"He was eighty-seven, Mr. Pons."

"I have no doubt there were differences between you."

"I suppose there were bound to be. Old people are occasionally unreasonable. But nothing very serious, Mr. Pons. Certainly nothing serious enough to bring him to make such a change in his will."

"Your grandfather was in good health?"

"He had been failing for some years, Mr. Pons. No, I shouldn't say he was in good health—or had been in the past three years. He was—well, uncertain on his legs, as one would say."

"Shaky, Miss Morris?"

"Yes, sir, He still got around, but only with difficulty."

"You are mentioned here, Miss Morris—for five hundred pounds."

"I know, Mr. Pons. That was the exact sum my grandfather once mentioned he would leave Percy."

"Indeed. Excuse me, Miss Morris."

Pons got up and went over to that corner of our quarters in which he kept his chemical paraphernalia. He sat down there and carefully scrutinized one page after another of the will Miss Morris had given him, using a magnifying glass, and putting the pages over light, one atop the other. Mrs. Johnson assured Miss Morris *sotto voce,* while they waited, that Pons was a great detective who could unravel any problem at all, but Miss Morris did not seem entirely convinced.

Presently Pons returned to his chair at the fireplace. "There are two courses open to you, Miss Morris. You can contest this will, or you can lay a claim to wages covering the years you took care of your grandfather—unless, of course, he paid you a salary."

"Oh, no, Mr. Pons—short of providing my living, he paid me nothing. Then, uncertainly, she added, "Which would you do, Mr. Pons?"

"Contest, by all means!"

"But how can I do so, Mr. Pons? I *know* that is my grandfather's signature."

"Very well. Let us accept that it *is* indeed Mr. Lemuel Morris's signature. But this will, Miss Morris, is a forgery."

"How can you say so!" cried Miss Morris.

"Each of four pages has been signed in precisely the same way. There is not the slightest deviation among the signatures. One is a precise copy of the other. I submit, Miss Morris, that no man of eighty-seven—and certainly not a man who was shaky—could possibly perform such a feat. I am far from that age myself, and I never to my knowledge indite my name in exactly the same way twice in succession. Nor does Dr. Parker. No, Miss Morris—I rather suspect that your cousin Percy is at the bottom of it. You need only apply to a competent solicitor and lay these facts before him. There are plenty of capable experts who will present the court with all the proof necessary."

Mrs. Johnson beamed, as if her faith in Pons's infallibility had been proved.

3 December 1919

Pons on Probability. "Though there are always several possible or probable solutions to every problem, there is only one that will exactly fit all the facts. One proceeds initially to apply the facts to the solution that seems most likely in the circumstances, and then, if they do not fit, to one after another until the correct solution is found.

"If, however, all the probable solutions are eliminated—if none fits all the facts—then whatever remains, no matter how improbable, must be the correct solution. This was the course invariable followed by the Master. In my opinion, no other course is proper for an investigator.

"Occasionally the police, before they fall back upon this method, seize upon the most likely solution as the correct one, and then attempt to make the facts fit the solution. This has had the happy result of bringing to my attention problems I might not otherwise have encountered."

11 December 1919

When Pons came to the breakfast table this morning I had

the satisfaction of reading a lead in the morning paper to him. " 'Morris Will Case: Percy Morris Charged.' "

"Ah, that young woman took the most sensible course," observed Pons. "I was inclined to think her a little soft—perhaps ready to accept some compromise from her cousin. I am delighted that it is not so."

"Why?" I asked.

"It is a simple matter of seeing justice done, my dear fellow," he replied. "There is a great deal being said today about rehabilitation rather than punishment. I have dealt with the criminal element long enough to know that this idealistic humanitarianism takes rise out of ignorance rather than any well-founded knowledge. Rehabilitation is fine theory, but let us have punishment first."

I could not help observing that my companion sounded like a character from *Alice in Wonderland.*

He ignored me, as he often does. "There is, too, an abundance of prattle about guilt. 'Crime and the criminal are the fault of society,' and it follows to these people who talk in this manner, that 'the criminal is not responsible, society is.' Now, it would be idle to deny that poverty and filth are fertile soil for crime, but it is nothing short of lunacy to suggest that it follows upon this admission that *all* crime rises from such a background, and that all criminals are therefore free of social responsibility. But this ridiculous claim is being made by ever noisier elements of our society. The denial of personal responsibility is fatuous. I do not know a single jurist of my considerable acquaintance who will subscribe to such nonsense."

"You cannot very well rehabilitate a man who has been hanged," I said.

"Ah, well, if he deserved hanging in the first place, there is very little that can be said in favor of trying to rehabilitate him. We are coming dangerously close to a world in which everything is done in behalf of the law-breaker—and at the expense of the law-abiding citizen. That is the road to anarchic chaos. It is the end result of indulgence in idealistic sentimentality, not of rational thought. We have always had the conflict between the individual and society, and the ultimate goal is to protect society by legal means at the least possible loss to the rights of the individual. But as the earth's population increases, it becomes inevitable that the rights of the individual must give way increasingly to the well-being of the social structure as a whole. Yet here we see the beginnings of a movement that goes counter to this inescapable fact—the outcry is for the protection of the rights of precisely those elements of society who have forfeited their right to demand such protection by anti-social acts. We are reversing Darwin—by insisting that the unfit survive."

I thought him unduly harsh and said as much.

He brushed this aside impatiently. "It is not a matter of harshness or softness. It is simply a failure to see the forest for the trees. Miss Morris's counsel has certainly taken the correct course. Contesting the forged will meant charging the forger. He should get what is coming to him, though, in view of what happens in our courts all too often, it may be thought infantile to expect adequate justice."

14 December 1919

Pons was speaking of the commonplaceness of the average crime this morning when Inspector Jamison paid us a visit.

"I put it to you, Jamison," said Pons, "is it not true that the majority of capital crimes committed in England are utterly without imagination?"

Jamison nodded. "Dull, if I may say so. Very dull. Of course, it's not every crime that has one of these private inquiry agents hanging about to colour it up a bit."

"*Touché!*" cried Pons.

"It's little more most of the time than some bloke breaking in and killing a man in the course of a robbery—or a man killing his wife out of jealousy or something of that kind—open and shut cases. The only trouble we have is in the courts—we know we've got our man, but counsel confuses everybody."

Pons smiled. "What problem troubles you today, Jamison?"

"This is just a friendly call," said the Inspector, faintly indignant.

"Not a mystery to be solved in all London?" pressed Pons with a note of disappointment in his voice.

Jamison shook his head. "We've had three murders and one accidental death in the past week."

"All solved, I take it," said Pons dryly.

Jamison hedged a little. "We've got one murderer—and we're onto the other two."

"Capital!" exclaimed Pons. "And the accidental death?"

"Ah, that's a miserable business," said Jamison. "Young woman fell off a train on the London, Brighton and South Coast Railway on Sunday night."

"I don't recall reading about it in the papers."

"I believe it would make nothing more than a small paragraph on the inside pages," said Jamison.

"I see by your preoccupied air and the way you finger your vest button, Jamison, you're not happy about it."

"She was badly injured, Pons—fractured skull, one leg cut off."

"How old was she?"

"Just twenty-three. I'd have called her a good-looking woman. Angela Morell. A clerk in a dairy in Lavender Hill."

"Go on," urged Pons.

"The body was found in Merstham tunnel. There seems to be no question but that a fall from the train was the cause of her death. None. She couldn't have fallen from any train but the 9:13 P.M. from London Bridge to Brighton, or the 9:33 P.M. from Charing Cross to Reading. But both these trains came out of the tunnel with all carriage doors shut. I don't know what kind of feat it would be to fall from a carriage and shut the door behind you. It may not be impossible."

"But it is certainly improbable," conceded Pons.

"Then, too, she had a bit of veil in her mouth."

"Her hat had a veil attached?"

"None."

"Ah," said Pons, his interest quickening.

"Caught on a tooth, in fact."

"A gag."

"Perhaps. But let us say somebody pushed her. Then we come up to the question of why?—and who?"

"I take it she was unmarried."

Jamison nodded.

"You've traced her movements?"

"That's routine, as you know. She left her lodgings at seven that night, saying she was going for only a short walk, and would be back within the hour. But one of her friends said that in the afternoon she had looked through a railway time-table."

"She had an assignation then," suggested Pons. "Was she accustomed to walking out?"

"The landlady said she had two gentlemen friends. But there were nights when she went out alone. She was always back by eleven on such nights. She didn't speak of them to anyone."

"Assuming that she permitted two gentlemen to call for her openly, there must then have been a strong reason why she should be clandestine with a third—*if* her assignation was with a man."

"Why do you intimate it may not have been?"

"I wonder what manner of man carries a veil about with him. But I am out of touch with the world of fashion."

"No, no, it's true—a woman would be more likely to carry a veil."

"A woman perhaps who had followed her husband to a clandestine meeting with another woman."

"You are certainly colouring it up, Pons," said Jamison.

"Ah, well, if you are content with a verdict of accidental death, there is surely no need to pursue the matter further. I submit, however, that you are anything but satisfied with that verdict. Let us be as objective as we can about the matter. We are given a young women—not ill-favored in looks—who is attractive enough to appeal to members of the opposite sex. She goes off to what must certainly be an assignation and is found dead. Very well, then. Eliminating accidental death, we are left with suicide or murder. Had she any patent reason for suicide?"

"We are aware of none."

"Then we come back to murder. Certain limited possibilities are open to us. Though the young woman had been careful to maintain a reputation for good character, we do not have in hand any proof that she was indeed a woman of good character. She could have been conducting a liaison with a married man—and fallen victim either to him or his wife. She could have been a prostitute engaged in blackmailing selected victims, one of whom took this method of disposing of her. She could as easily have been followed by someone violently jealous of her liaison and murdered by him in a rage. Within the boundaries of the known facts we can hardly speculate farther without entering the realm of pure imagination. I submit, however, that the fragment of veil found in her mouth suggests a certain premeditation."

"A contrived accident is what you make it, Pons."

"I think it unlikely that it was accidental death," replied Pons. "The fragment of veil caught on her tooth and the closed carriage doors both suggest the presence of some other person in the compartment from which she was thrust. You saw the body?"

"A horrible sight."

"Were there any marks suggesting that her hands and feet had been tied?"

"None."

"Very well, then—she might have been stunned to keep her quiet, and gagged to prevent her crying out if she came to her senses before the tunnel was reached. I take it there was nothing to suggest robbery?"

"She was carrying five pounds and wore two rings—one a diamond, one a ruby."

"On the wages of a dairy clerk?"

Inspector Jamison was disconcerted.

"I put it to you, Jamison, it might be interesting to pursue the inquiry with the conviction that Miss Morell was murdered. Try to ascertain where she got on to the train, whether she was accompanied by anyone, and what her destination was. I rather suspect that the place of the assignation was in a specific compartment on the train, not on the platform, so that her murderer need take no chance of being seen with her."

After Inspector Jamison had gone, Pons said, "I take a dim view of the Yard's finding her murderer. That young woman, if indeed she had been engaged in some criminal activity or a course that would not meet with social approval, seems to have covered herself very well—so well, in fact, that she may defeat all attempts to discover the identity of her murderer. The kind of clandestine affair in which she may have been engaged is commonly extremely difficult to uncover."

21 December 1919

I touched Pons on a sensitive point today when I observed that the evidence offered to convict the Moat Farm murderer was almost entirely circumstantial.

"I seem to detect a note of disapproval, Parker," he said with some asperity. "Yet circumstantial evidence is the strongest of all possible evidence."

"As strong as the testimony of eye-witnesses?"

He chuckled dryly. "Stronger! Circumstances cannot lie. They may be misinterpreted, but they cannot lie. Eye-witnesses can, and do—sometimes by design, but usually because they are simply mistaken. I put it to you that no half dozen eye-witnesses will tell precisely the same story; their accounts are certain to

Solar Pons

Inspector Jamison

Alfred Peake

Dr. Parker and Solar Pons

vary. All things being relative, some will see a short man, some a tall one, some a fat one, some a thin man, some brown, some hazel, some blue, some green. But that is not so of circumstances."

"The outcry against circumstantial evidence cannot be that ill-founded," I protested.

"It can and it is. I suspect it was begun by criminals who were fairly caught by circumstances. Wills in *On Principles of Circumstantial Evidence* puts the case well when he says, 'The distinct and specific proving power of circumstantial evidence depends upon its incompatibility with any reasonable hypothesis other than that of the truth of the principal fact in proof of which it is adduced; so that, after the exhaustion of every other mode of solution, we must either conclude that the accused has been guilty of the act imputed, or renounce as illusory the results of consciousness and experience, and such knowledge as we possess of the workings of the human mind.' And Lord Coleridge, summing up in the trial of Dickman, the railway murderer, in 1910, said: 'If we find a variety of circumstances all pointing in the same direction, convincing in proportion to the number and variety of those circumstances and their independence one of another, although each separate piece of evidence, standing by itself, may admit of an innocent interpretation, yet the cumulative effect of such evidence may be overwhelming evidence of guilt.' I recognize no intelligent argument that runs counter to these statements."

"Why, we read interminably of the police trying to convict on evidence that is demolished readily enough by counsel," I said.

"I fear that is only too true. I submit, nevertheless, that you are taking issue with a police action, or the flawed decision of the prosecution. That is a matter of attempting to make of circumstances what they are not. I have no sympathy with it—but it does not bear any relation to the proper interpretation and use of circumstantial evidence."

"But surely you cannot deny that circumstantial evidence takes strength from inference, and that is a matter of opinion."

"It is opinion supported by facts. Indeed, it is opinion rising out of the available facts. I think, if you care to examine the records, you will find that far more wrong convictions have resulted from false and mistaken direct and positive testimony than from the wrong inferences drawn from circumstantial evidence. No one fact is employed alone in the building of a case on circumstantial evidence; no, it is the accumulation of facts that, taken together, related together, are so strong as to establish a clear indication of guilt. Compared to the fallibility of human beings, circumstances invariably present the stronger case."

23 December 1919

Pons's wholehearted respect for time was clearly demonstrated today. Having no problem to engage him, he spent the entire day adding to his store of knowledge, which far exceeds my own. He reads reference books, once he had done with the papers—the current issue of *Whitaker's Almanack*—Skeat's *Concise Etymological Dictionary of the English Language*—*A Dictionary of Dates*—Isaac Taylor's *Words and Places*—*Whitaker's Perrage*—a guide to the cathedrals of France—certainly a hodgepodge of books on a singular variety of subjects.

Seeing me observing him, he smiled and said, "Nothing is as unique as a fact, my dear fellow, and nothing as fascinating. You and I—indeed, the entire universe, depends on facts."

"It is even more fascinating to realize what some people make of facts," I said.

"Is it not!" he agreed, his eyes twinkling.

27 December 1919

A note today from Jamison.

" 'In regard to that Merstham tunnel murder,' " Pons read, interjecting, "Aha! he now clearly calls it 'murder'!—'the woman Morell appears to have been involved with a number of men from her past. New evidence suggests that she has been blackmailing them. A search of her room turned up a small notebook with seventeen names—two of them women. No addresses, but we'll find them. Curious notations under each name indicating payments. Apparently none ever came to her address—she met them by appointment. It will take time, but we'll find him (or her!) eventually. Other than these occasional appointments, her life in Lavender Hill would seem to have been straightforward enough.' " Pons's eyes twinkled as he dropped the note into the coal scuttle at the fireplace. "I daresay Jamison will have it, in time to come, we coloured it up a bit."

7 January 1920

Mrs. Johnson this morning showed up to our quarters a clergyman who had sent ahead his card announcing himself as the Reverend Howard Foster. He proved to be a lean shank of a man, with a face like a closed rat trap, very dour and grim. His jaws were clamped together, and his bushy sideburns, now greying, were wiry and stiff. He wore clerical garb, withal a trifle shiny from wear, and carried an unbrella rolled up under his arm, though the day was fair and rather cold.

He addressed himself forthrightly to Pons. "I am taking the liberty, sir, of bringing to you a small problem which I believe is not one for the police. I understand you have some little knowledge in these matters."

"There are those who say so," admitted Pons.

The Reverend Foster drew from the inner pocket of his long black coat an envelope which he handed to Pons.

"Addressed to a lady," ventured Pons. "And in type."

"My niece."

Pons opened the envelope and took out the paper inside. From where I sat, it appeared to be a half page of proof or print. It was ragged along one edge, as if it had been torn from a book.

Pons narrowed his eyes. A kind of gleam came into them. He gazed provocatively at our visitor.

"My niece received this yesterday by post. I was in the study when she opened it. She gazed at it, and I presume she read it. Her face went pale. Then she moaned softly and ran—no, let me amend that, Mr. Pons—she tottered from the room. I ran to her aid, but she thrust me aside. I begged her to tell me what the matter was, but all she did was shake her head and say, 'It's no use. I must go away—far away!' Since then she has hardly come from her room and I have not had a word from her. She walks about like a dead woman. Can you make anything of that? I picked it up when she dropped it, but I cannot make head or tail of it save that it appears to be from a book—not the kind of text that I with my limited time would be likely to read."

"I will need a little time to examine it," said Pons. "I take it your niece has not always lived with you?"

"Only since the death of my wife short of two years ago. She came back unexpectedly from America. She had gone there in 1910 intending to return in a few years, but the war caught her there, and she stayed until it was no longer dangerous to come back. Her father—her last surviving parent, my brother—had died in the meantime; so she naturally came to live with me."

"Ah, she is then no longer a very young woman."

"She is thirty-four."

Pons glanced again at the envelope. "Posted in London. And not far away." He looked up. "I see that you have come up from the country, since the address on the envelope is obviously your home. Presumably you have other errands in London. If you will stop around in an hour or two, I believe I may have some explanation of this mysterious communication."

The clergyman moved as if dismissed by his bishop.

He had hardly left our quarters—indeed, his footsteps could still be heard on the stairs—before Pons subjected me to one of those little games he enjoys playing so much. He thrust the page from the envelope at me.

"What do you make of that, Parker?" he asked.

I had only to glance at it to say, "It is clearly a page torn from a book."

"No, no," cried Pons vigorously. "It is clearly a torn page—but not necessarily from a book. Have a closer look at it."

I read it with care—

> "Faithless Dick," said Silver. "I've a gauge on the keg of rum, mind, wretch. There's the key; fill a pannikin and bring it up."
>
> Terrified as I was, I could not help thinking to myself that this way Mr. Arrow will have got the strong waters that destroyed him.
>
> Dick was not to come for a while, and during his lengthy absence Israel spoke straight and soft for the cook to hear. I caught but a word or two—"I" and "you", yet I gathered some very important news, that it was certain that not all the crew could be made to join in a mutiny against the captain or yet in any crew of John Silver's, no matter what the circumstances. It made me feel good to hear, and I knew that whatever happened there was still time to stand with valor against Silver.
>
> End of Chapter XI:
> What I Heard in the Apple Barrel.

When I looked up, Pons's eyes were keen upon me, and dancing with delight. "Now, then, what do you make of it?"

"It is surely no mystery," I said, sure of myself. "I know the book from which it comes very well—and it *is* a book."

"Is it, indeed?"

His sharpness ought to have given me pause. "Yes—and you ought to be able to name it as well as I. Wherever else would you find 'Mr. Arrow' and 'John Silver' but in *Treasure Island?*"

"Where else, indeed! Where else but in that miserable revision of the concluding paragraphs of chapter eleven!"

"What do you mean?" I cried. "I remember the scene well.

Jim has fallen asleep in the apple barrel, and when he wakes learns for the first time what a scoundrel Long John Silver is—planning the mutiny and the murder of Squire Trelawney. It is one of my favorite books. That is the way the chapter ends."

"On the contrary," said Pons, with that air I had found so annoying, of being inevitably right. "It ends with the voice of the look-out shouting 'Land-ho!' "

Even as as he said it, I knew that it was with these words that the chapter did indeed end.

"Whatever Stevenson was not, he was not a careless stylist, was he, Parker?"

"I should not say so."

"Indeed not. Fancy his having written—I commend the fourth line to your attention—the 'way Mr. Arrow will have got the strong waters that destroyed him.' 'Will have got' indeed! Stevenson would never have been guilty of such a construction."

I conceded the point. "But it is clearly in print," I said, a trifle bewildered now.

"Ah, Parker, I fear you share the common man's reverence for print. He will tell you, 'I saw it in the paper!' as if this were the final bit of proof needed to support whatever contention he may have uttered. 'I saw it in print'—sometimes it is 'cold print', though all print is by its very nature cold; if it has any warmth it is the author's artistry, not the printer's."

I looked at the page again. "Then," I said, venturing boldly into Pons's domain, "then clearly that construction was necessary to the printer!"

"Capital! Capital!" cried Pons, clasping his hands together and raising them aloft as in tribute to heaven or to himself—certainly not to me. "You have begun to learn the elements of ratiocination. The printer is not an illiterate, yet he prints such a construction as this. Why?"

Thus emboldened, I ventured again. "The lines contain some message which the woman—Miss Foster—could read."

"That is a trifle elementary, Parker," said Pons, a little more subdued. "I should have thought that anyone so familiar with and fond of *Treasure Island* could have read the message at once. At first glance."

"You flatter me," I said, with an edge of sarcasm I could not withhold.

"Not in the slightest," he said, adding generously, "You do certainly possess the intelligence, you are just not applying it. This is a simple hidden message—I should not call it a cipher, it is too elementary."

"I fail to see it."

"Let us just have a look at a copy of *Treasure Island.*" So saying, he got up and found the book among the jumble on his shelves. He was turning to chapter eleven as he came back to his chair. "Ah, here is the first line. ' "Dick," said Silver, "I trust you." '—but this hapless specimen has ' "Faithless Dick" ' —why?"

"Because 'faithless' was necessary to him," I said firmly.

"Then if that absurd construction in the fourth line was also necessary, and if, obviously, 'faithless' must then be the first word of any message this page conveys, the whole should be plain as a pikestaff."

He got up and put the Stevenson novel away again. Then he came to stand before me, lighting a pipe of the shag he smoked, and watching me struggle with the hidden message the page contained.

"A certain order must necessarily be imposed upon even the crudest concealed message," said Pons. "In this one it is precisely as mathematical—if not as intricate—as in one of His Majesty's secret codes. Have a go at it, Parker."

"I am studying it," I said.

"Let me point out again that we have two words—'faithless' and 'will'—begin with them."

"Why must it be 'will'?" I asked. Why can it not be 'will have'?"

"One word at a time, Parker," said Pons with infinite patience. " 'Faithless' is the first word, is it not?"

"You have said it must be, and it stands to reason that it is," I agreed.

"And it is in the first line."

"Elementary," I said.

"And 'will' is in the fourth line."

"And it is the fourth word," I said.

And there for a few moments—long enough to permit Pons to sigh and wonder with evident pity if all my teachers had so difficult a time with me—I stuck, and then, of course, it came to me. I had been searching for something more complex, but the simplicity of it deceived me. With "faithless" as the first word in the first line, and "will" the fourth word in the fourth line, I tried the second word in the second line and the third in the third and had "Faithless wretch I will" and from there went rapidly down the lines and read it aloud with a shout of triumph.

"Faithless wretch, I will come for you all in good time!"

"I congratulate you, Parker," said Pons. "A trifle slow, but you came through. Now then, who wrote it?"

"You have me there, Pons."

"Do not say so. A printer wrote it."

"I concede that a printer set it, but how do you know he wrote it?"

"Why, because he is an American."

"An American!" I cried. "Pons, you are making sport of me. That is a *non sequitur* if I ever heard one."

"My dear fellow, I try manfully to avoid *non sequiturs.* Would any Englishman have set 'valour' in that American fashion?—'valor'? Not on your life. Even if an American had handed the copy in so, he would have spelled it 'valour'. So it follows that the American set it himself."

"With every day that passes, you amaze me more," I said, knowing how it would please him.

He bowed. "With so well grounded a beginning, you will do as well in no time at all."

"To say nothing of so good an instructor," I added.

But at this moment our little game was interrupted by the return of our client, too impatient to remain away for even an hour. I opened the door to his knock.

"Come in, come in, my dear Reverend Foster," cried Pons. "Pray be seated."

"I trust you have some information for me, Mr. Pons," said the clergyman, seating himself in the chair Pons thrust forward.

"I fear I may have some unpleasant news, sir," said Pons, taking his stand with one arm on the mantel. "It depends upon some intelligence you may be able to convey to me."

"If I can," said our client.

"It is about Miss Cordelia. Pray tell me, was she married?"

Our client's face expressed some dismay. "If so, I do not know of it."

"How was she occupied during her years in the United States?"

"She was employed in a printer's and stationer's shop in New York."

"And if not married, engaged in a liaison," said Pons.

The Reverend Foster's face flushed angrily.

Pons gave him no opportunity to speak. "One or the other, and she feared to tell you, knowing your restrictive views. She left the man—husband or lover—and returned to England. We do not know why. She may have had just cause. Now he has followed and found her and he has sent her this message."

"What message?"

" 'Faithless wretch, I will come for you all in good time.' It has an ominous sound, sir. By its very nature, it suggests that some sort of bond exists between the sender and your niece. I submit that they were or are married. He means to frighten her and uses a simple code she must have known and apprehended instantly. See there —"he took the page from my hands as he spoke, and pointed out the words of the message"—how it is framed. For some reason, they used this code to communicate in earlier years. It may well have been a legitimate reason. I am not prepared to say."

Anger, bewilderment, disbelief—plainly our client was unwilling to entertain the thought that his niece had been involved with a man in any disreputable matter.

"This is, indeed, a matter for the police, Reverend Foster," said Pons quietly. "I suggest you repair to them without delay and ask them to find an American printer not long employed in London, in the area from which this message was posted. He will be a man very likely not over forty, one who cannot resist gloating, vain and perhaps ill-tempered, for only such a one would so taunt and frighten a woman."

Our client folded the page and thrust it back into its envelope, and this in turn he put into his pocket. He got up. "I will need to think of this for a while, Mr. Pons. I had better put it to my niece."

"Do not delay," warned Pons.

"Not such a man as would inspire confidence in a young woman," said Pons reflectively after he had gone. "One confined by a narrow view of the world. That poor woman must carry her burden alone."

9 January 1920

I watched Pons today as he read the paper. The process never varies.

He turns first to the political news, scans it briefly, then to news of the international scene. He reads this too, only cursorily.

But any account of a crime enlists his undivided attention. He will sit tugging at the lobe of his left ear, long after he has read the account, his eyes staring right through the paper. Manifestly, he is turning the problem of the crime over in his mind.

Now and then he makes some comment at random about the "blindness" or the "stupidity" of the police.

More rarely, he commends them, with, "The police are not all fools, thank heaven!"

Having read the paper, he gets the scissors and cuts out any account of a crime that interests him and adds it to his voluminous scrapbook.

The paper is then discarded. He assumes invariably that I have already read it, whether or not it is so.

11 January 1920

A grim-faced Pons greeted me when I came in from my morning round today.

"Have you seen the paper?" he asked.

"I had an early confinement," I answered, shaking my head.

Without a word he passed the paper to me, folded so as to emphasize a few paragraphs under the heading, *Tragedy in Herts.*

"Westmill, Herts," I read. "Miss Cordelia Foster, niece of the Rev. Howard Foster, was seriously wounded last night by a mysterious gun-shot, as she walked across the lawn toward the rectory. Her assailant was concealed behind a hedge that separated the lawn from a small formal garden.

"An American printer, Clarence Farwell, employed by Messrs. Godwin of London, W. 2, is being held. The American claims that Miss Foster is his wife, and that she deserted him. Miss Foster has denied his claim, stating that Mr. Farwell was previously married.

"Inquiries are under way."

"I was afraid that fellow Foster would do nothing," said Pons. "If he put it to her, she very probably denied it, and he accepted her denial at face value because he wished to do so, out of some desire to avoid a challenge to his concept of morality. A foolish man, whose pride has led to this."

14 January 1920

The Adventure of the Bookseller's Clerk. Pons called me over to the windows looking down into Praed Street this morning. "What do you make of that fellow?" he asked.

Below, on the kerb, stood an elderly man, clad in a foreign-looking fur cap, and a long coat, with a thick scarf wound around his neck and hanging out over his coat. Even through the light snow falling, I could see that his shoes were very definitely British. Moreover, they were wet.

"He has been walking for some distance," I said.

"Or some time," amended Pons. "In so light a snowfall it would of necessity be one or the other."

"At the moment he is studying 7B. I suppose he may be a client."

"I should think that likely."

"He looks like a countryman," I ventured.

"I think not," said Pons. "That is not a countryman's garb."

"He seems to be in no hurry."

"True. But at the same time he appears not to have shaved this morning; it is possible that he left home in some agitation."

"But it is almost noon. He couldn't have come directly here," I protested.

"He may be a shopkeeper who had to wait upon his assistant to arrive. Or he may have closed early for the noon hour. But see, he has decided to come in. We shall hear what he has to say."

In a few moments we heard his heavy tread on the stair, preceded by the lighter footfalls of Mrs. Johnson. And presently he stood on the threshold introducing himself.

"Mr. Pons? My name is Jason Brompton."

"A dealer in second-hand books," said Pons.

"I am, indeed. Perhaps you have been in my shop in Edgware Road."

"No, Mr. Brompton. The mustiness of old books is unmistakable. Pray sit down and tell me how I can be of assistance to you."

Mr. Brompton came forward and sat down somewhat stiffly near the fireplace where Pons stood with his back to the mantel, his hands in the pockets of his dressing-gown.

"Well, sir, it's an old man's fancies, I'm sure, but the fact is I'm troubled about my assistant, Dennis Golders. I very much fear he lives beyond his means—and I don't understand how he can do so. I knew him to be in poor circumstances when he applied for the position, and while I cannot pay him very much—times are difficult, Mr. Pons; one need not buy books, as I am sure you know—he has begun to spend far more on clothes than he earns. They are made for him, Mr. Pons, in Bond Street!"

He said this as if he were speaking of some personage far above his station.

"He may have come into a legacy."

"No, sir. I would certainly know it if he had."

"How long has he been with you?"

"Two years."

"His work is evidently satisfactory."

"Indeed, it is. I have no complaint."

"His accounts are in order?"

"Perfectly. My concern, I assure you, is for his welfare. I cannot rest until I learn how he comes by such means as to make it possible for him to live far beyond the scale even I can afford."

"How did he come to you?"

"He applied with the best references."

"From other book-sellers?"

"Oh, no, sir. He had held various other positions—if I may say so—considerably better than the one for which he made application; but he professed to a love for books—and that is not uncommon in our trade, Mr. Pons, and, since my shop has a good clientele, and has been there for many years—you may have heard of Brompton's—he came with the intention of learning the business."

"Who referred him, Mr. Brompton?" pressed Pons.

"Lord Arthur Savile, for one."

Pons' eyebrows shot up; his eyes began to twinkle. "Indeed!" he said. "Who else?"

"Sir William Joynson-Hicks, H. G. Wells, and Lord Northcliffe."

Pons preserved an almost mask-like face. "I should very much like to see his references, Mr. Brompton."

Mr. Brompton's grizzled face broke into a broad smile. "I rather thought you would, Mr. Pons. I have them here."

He produced four letters from a letter-case in his pocket.

Pons unfolded one after the other and read them. His face remained inscrutable. Presently he looked up.

"Mr. Golders is now at work?"

"Yes, Mr. Pons."

"How many other clerks do you employ, Mr. Brompton?"

"One who comes in evenings, when I have open hours. And a part-time clerk, when one or the other of us must be away."

"If you can arrange to remain away from the shop for an hour longer this noon, Dr. Parker and I will walk around to Brompton's."

"Oh, that is easily done, Mr. Pons. Mr. Golders—with uncommon thrift—always brings his own lunch, thus giving me a considerable latitude insofar as time is concerned. I have appreciated it."

"And if I may, I will retain these references for the time being."

Mr. Brompton looked a little dubious, but he assented readily enough.

"If you will step around this afternoon, I may possibly be able to satisfy your concern about Mr. Golders," said Pons.

Once Mr. Brompton had taken his leave, Pons began to chuckle. His eyes now positively danced.

"Have you ever before encountered such bedfellows as those

gentlemen who gave Mr. Dennis Golders references, Parker?" he asked.

"Well, they are impressive. I don't, though, know Sir William Joynson-Hicks."

Pon's laughter burst forth. "Your indifference to politics causes you to miss some considerable entertainment. That fellow Joynson-Hicks is quite possibly the most jingoistic, egotistic ass who ever brayed in the halls of any government in the world."

"But the others, of course, I know. Indeed, I have a signed *Tono-Bungay.*"

Pons sobered once more. "By all means produce it."

"I have it in my trunk," I said, and got up to get it.

It was not without some pride of possession that I laid the book before Pons, open to Well's signature.

Pons unfolded Well's letter of reference and laid it beside the autograph in *Tono-Bungay*.

"Identical," I said.

"Let us compare Northcliffe's signature," said Pons. "Any copy of the *Daily Mail* will do."

He found the paper and presently discovered the newspaper magnate's signature—the bold *Northcliffe* on the editorial page.

"They are certainly the same," I admitted.

"And we may assume that Sir William Joynson-Hicks's signature is as genuine," said Pons. "But Lord Arthur Savile's is another matter entirely."

"You are more familiar with the peerage than I," I said. "The name means nothing to me."

"Lord Arthur Savile," said Pons, "is a character in a mediocre short story by Oscar Wilde. I daresay Mr. Dennis Golders is not entirely lacking a sense of humor."

"And Mr. Brompton is not as familiar with his stock in trade as he ought to be."

"Oh, I would not say so. It is just such a name as Mr. Brompton must certainly have heard, but, since it appears in a relatively trivial work of fiction, it is not such a one as he might readily relate to its source, and, coming upon it as the signature to a letter, might quite conceivably conclude that the writer was a peer of the realm."

"What cheek that fellow Golders must have!"

"If you can forego lunch, Parker, let us just walk around to Brompton's and have a few words with Mr. Golders."

"By all means!" I said.

But Pons was not quite ready. He fancied a disguise. He laboriously affixed sideboards, changed his clothes to rather severe garb, and clapped a pince-nez on a black ribbon to his nose and a bowler to his head.

"You look," I said, "like a private enquiry agent dressed up to resemble a businessman."

"That is close enough," said Pons. "Let us be off."

Mr. Dennis Golders was of rather shorter than average height. He was a blonde, well-built young man, alert and bright-eyed. When we entered Brompton's, he did not thrust himself upon us, but permitted us to browse among the shelves and bins of books. There were two other customers in the shop, but these presently bought books and departed.

Only then, seeing that we had not evidently found anything to our liking, did the clerk approach us.

"May I help you, sir?" he asked Pons, since it was plainly Pons who seemed to be in search of something.

"Thank you, I think not," answered Pons crisply.

"You are obviously a bibliophile," said Golders.

"Ah, is it so patent?"

"If I may say so. You must, then, have favorite authors."

"Hardy, Keats, Byron, Shelley, Dickens, Meredith." Pons rattled these names off with a professional air.

"I may have something for you, sir," pursued Golders. "But it will come rather dear."

Pons's eyes narrowed. "Price is no object," he said, though his attitude belied it.

"Let me show it to you."

Golders plunged into the rear of the shop where, reaching behind shelves of books which were separated from the wall of the shop by a counter, he drew forth a book which he handed to Pons.

I saw that it was Dickens's *Nicholas Nickleby* in fair condition.

Pons glanced at Golders rather than at the book. "A first edition?" he hazarded.

"No, sir. But it will cost four pounds just the same."

"Four pounds!" cried Pons.

"Please open it to the flyleaf, sir."

Pons did so.

Disclosed on the flyleaf was the autograph of Charles Dickens, with a line of greeting and the date.

"Aha!" murmured Pons. "Indeed, I do want this. Four pounds is a trifle dear, as you say—but a signed Dickens!"

He handed the book back to Golders to be wrapped, while he himself took four pound notes from his pocket and laid them on the counter.

"Do you by any chance have anything more like this?" asked Pons.

There was the barest hesitation in Golders's businesslike wrapping of *Nicholas Nickleby*. Then he resumed, as he said, "These items are not commonly come upon, sir. Once in a great while we buy a library with such a treasure among the books, but it is not a frequent occurrence. You might look in again. Of course, some modern authors like Hardy and Conrad are more readily found in signed copies, but Dickens is less readily discovered."

"But this is surely not the only signed book on the premises," persisted Pons.

"We-ell, no, it isn't," admitted Golders.

"Then, if you have another, let me see it," demanded Pons impatiently.

Having completed his parcel, the clerk reached behind the same shelf of books and came out with another.

This time it was H. G. Wells's *The First Men in the Moon,* the Newnes edition of 1901. It bore but a simple, undated signature.

"How much?" asked Pons.

Golders seemed visibly to take Pons's measure. "I realize Wells may not be one of your favorites, sir, but there are those who collect him. Two pounds six."

Pons paid it with no more than a grimace.

"If you are interested in stopping in from time to time—preferably at this hour, sir," said Golders, as we went out, "I may have other such treasures for you to examine."

"Extraordinary luck!" I said, as we walked along Edgware Road toward Praed Street. "That you should be able to acquire two such signed books!"

"You did not think it unusual?"

"No. Many such treasures are in fact lost in private libraries. Only the owner knows they are there. Once the owner dies, however, it is another matter, for in many cases his heirs are not aware of everything on the shelves. That is particularly true if the library is a large one. Thus, it is eminently possible for a dealer like Brompton—who buys up entire libraries to keep stock on his shelves—to get hold of such books at a very reasonable price and make a fair profit. Though these did seem to me more dear than the average."

"Well, let us just have a closer look at them when we have them home," said Pons, and would say no more.

Once back in our quarters, Pons compared the signature in the Wells he had bought with that in my *Tono-Bungay.* He scrutinized them under a magnifying glass. I did the same. There was no significant difference between them, save that the one in the book he had just bought seemed to be an older signature in that the letters were slightly larger than the signature in my book, and they had clearly been written with different pens.

"Would you say they were written by the same man?" asked Pons.

"I would indeed."

Pons turned next to the Dickens. He examined it thoroughly, from the front matter to the rear of the book. Then he handed it to me with the adjuration, "Pray examine the inside of the front cover, Parker."

"It is blank," I said.

"Say not so. Look again."

I studied it with care. It was somewhat stained, as by age and exposure, and the edges were rubbed.

"Does it not seem to you that an erasure has been made in the upper left corner?" asked Pons.

"The original price seems to have been removed," I said at last, detecting the area of the erasure.

"And what does it seem to you that price was?"

"Two and six."

"Two shillings sixpence," repeated Pons. "For a book signed by Dickens?"

"Obviously the book was so priced before the signature was discovered," I said.

"It may be so. We shall just wait upon Mr. Brompton to tell us."

So saying, he retired behind the morning newspaper.

Our client returned at two o'clock. He had had his lunch and he was now eager to return to his shop.

"I have been away far too long, Mr. Pons," he said, a little breathless from the exertion of climbing the stairs to our quarters.

"I fancy young Mr. Golders will not take it amiss," said Pons.

"He is a model of propriety," said Brompton. "But I hope you may have something to tell me of his means."

Without a word Pons put before him the signed copy of *Nicholas Nickleby*.

Brompton picked it up and turned it round in his hands. "Ah, you bought this in my shop. Two and six. But surely you don't want it. You must let me reimburse you."

"Four pounds," said Pons.

Our client dropped the book as if it had turned to hot coal in his hands. "Not in my shop!" he cried.

"But indeed." Pons bent, picked up the book, and thrust it again at Brompton. "Pray look at the flyleaf."

Brompton did so. His eyes bulged. His mouth fell open. He was manifestly astounded.

His hands trembling, he laid the book carefully down on the table. He took a deep, gulping breath before he spoke.

"Mr. Pons, I had no such book in my shop."

Pons bent again, flipped back the cover, and pointed to the spot where the original price had been erased.

"Look there, Mr. Brompton. The indentation is clear enough. Was that in your hand?"

"It seems to be my script," said Brompton. He leaned back in his chair. "But I cannot understand it. It is seldom indeed that a signed book comes into the shop."

"Do you to your knowledge have any signed books?"

"Well, yes, I have a Machen and a de la Mare. I had a Hardy, but Mr. Golders sold it and at a good price."

"Duly entered?"

"Yes, sir. I know my stock, and the entry was proper."

"You have not had a signed Wells?"

"No, Mr. Pons."

"Like this? Pons produced *The First Men in the Moon.*

"That looks like the book I had in stock. Not signed, of course. One and six."

Once again Pons opened the book, revealing the signature.

Our client grew pale, then flushed redly.

"I submit, Mr. Brompton, that if you now return to your shop you will find these sales entered—*Nicholas Nickleby* at two and six, *The First Men in the Moon* at one and six. The difference between those prices and four pounds for the Dickens, and two pounds six shillings for the Wells has gone into

Mr. Golders's pocket. I submit further that it is by just such sales that Mr. Golders has been able to improve his standard of living over quite some time. Mr. Golders seems to have a considerable knowledge of graphology."

"That is forgery, Mr. Pons. I shall discharge him at once," cried Brompton, coming to his feet, swelling with indignation and purpose.

"Do not be too hasty, Mr. Brompton," said Pons. "Mr. Golders is apparently content to live on but a small measure of illegal gain, and out of some considerable talent and ingenuity."

"I shall give him in charge," said Mr. Brompton angrily. "But first—let me reimburse you." He reached for his pocket.

Pons stayed his hand. "Let me persuade Mr. Golders to reimburse me instead," he said. "When you return to the shop, wrap up a book—any book—and ask Mr. Golders to step around here after work to deliver it."

"If you say so, Mr. Pons. But I cannot continue to employ him."

"Let me just talk to him first."

Mr. Brompton assented, but unwillingly. "I have been taken in—and I cannot undertake to estimate how many of my customers may have been swindled."

He was still muttering angrily when he departed.

"I rather think Mr. Brompton is more angry at having been deceived than at discovering that some of his customers may have been mulcted of small sums," observed Pons.

Late that afternoon, Mr. Dennis Golders knocked.

Pons threw open the door and invited him in. Golders did not immediately see me, and, since Pons had removed his disguise, he did not recognize him.

"I am delivering a book from Brompton's," said he.

"Come in, Mr. Golders, come in," said Pons.

As soon as Golders had taken a few steps into our quarters, Pons closed the door and stood with his back against it.

At the same moment Golders caught sight of me. He started guiltily, but quickly composed himself.

"Those books on the table are yours, are they not, Mr. Golders?" asked Pons.

Golder's eyes dropped to the signed books Pons had left lying out.

"No, sir. They are yours," said Golders, his equanimity restored. "You bought them this noon. I recognize your voice now even without sideboards, bowler and eye-glasses."

Pons chuckled. "Pray sit down, Mr. Golders."

Golders did so, alert but unafraid.

Pons came away from the door. "You have a considerable talent in forgery, Mr. Golders."

"Can you prove it, sir?" asked Golders.

"Yes, yes—if need be, easily," said Pons. "But I am not interested in proving it."

"The return of your money then," said Golders. "And, of course, I will take along the books again."

"I think not," said Pons. "Tell me, Mr. Golders, have you ever thought of turning that remarkable talent of yours to honest accounting?"

Golders looked at Pons calculatingly. "You are sure you have something 'honest' in mind?"

Pons shook his head disapprovingly. "Ah, you are already challenging the honesty of everyone else on the basis of your temporary lack—I say 'temporary' hopefully."

"Is there an honest way?"

"I believe there is—and there may even be occasion in it for such flights of your fancy as the forging of Lord Arthur Savile's signature."

Golders grinned. "And at a decent salary?"

"Quite sufficient for the style to which you have become accustomed, Mr. Golders. Are you willing to try it?"

"I am, sir."

"I have written a note to my brother who is in the Foreign Office. There is a constant need for the services of someone with your uncommon skill in the cryptology department. Take it around there tomorrow, for your place at Brompton's has clearly become untenable."

"There is an alternative?"

"Indeed, yes. Mr. Brompton is ready to give you in charge. And I have these books against that contingency. I trust it will never be necessary to use them. Such skill ought to be put to good use."

Golders began to laugh. "Forging letters and signatures of diplomats, couriers, intelligence agents, eh?" he said. "I never thought of it. It is still forgery, though, however you look at it. I suppose it all depends upon one's point-of-view, Mr. Pons."

"As does all life, Mr. Golders," said Pons. "Good luck!"

Golders took his leave as jauntily as if he had not a care in the world.

23 January 1920

Pons announced today that his brother Bancroft had secured a provisional place in the Intelligence Division of the Admiralty for Dennis Golders, the book-seller's clerk who proved so adept at forging the names of an astonishing variety of gentlemen.

I could not keep from chaffing him a bit, for I had had some reservations about his course of action in regard to Golders.

"Surely that is a kind of rehabilitation," I said.

"I daresay it may be so looked upon," answered Pons.

"Do I not detect a certain inconsistency here?" I asked.

He shot a sharp glance in my direction. " 'A foolish consistency,' " he began to quote Emerson, but I interrupted him.

" ' . . is the hobgoblin of little minds.' Yes, I know. But let me quote another eminent authority—'Rehabilitation is fine in theory, but let us have punishment first.' By courtesy of Mr. Solar Pons."

Pons laughed heartily. "I fear you have me there. But does not that depend upon the nature of the crime?"

"You have not said so," I said. "As I recall it, you did not discriminate at all."

"The nature of the crime in the previous instance was a considerable fraud," said Pons. "I am sure that Golders can be prevailed upon to reimburse his victims. But there is a fine point here I rather think you have not taken into consideration."

"In other words," I put in caustically, "when it comes to punishment, there is all the difference in the world between a large fraud and a little one?"

"There is not the slightest difference in fact, but only in degree, and the difference in degree affects only the degree of punishment."

"But Golders is not being punished, as far as I can see."

Pons chuckled. "I had no idea you felt even more strongly than I about this matter," he said. "If it will ease your mind—or your conscience, whichever it is—Bancroft has had some long conversations with Golders. Golders is perfectly willing to reimburse the purchasers of his forgeries out of his salary. But, quite apart from the fact that he cannot remember all of them, there is that fine point you have not considered."

"Pray enlighten me," I said.

"Why, it is simply the attitude of the purchasers. I submit that not one in ten would appreciate being told he did not own, in fact, a signed copy of a book he treasures. Far rather ignorance than repayment! Collectors are a curious lot—and book collectors are in many ways the most curious of them all."

"But what if one of them discovers the fraud and demands his money back from Brompton?"

"Why, then, Brompton will reimburse him—and Golders will reimburse Brompton."

"And as for the others?"

"They have simply paid for the happiness of possessing a forged signature they do not recognize as a forgery. Their lack of knowledge does not in any way affect their happiness in its possession. I know, Parker, in the interests of propriety, you would disillusion them. But to what end? It would not satisfy them, it would in fact leave them, I submit, far more unhappy than they are in their possession of their elaborate forgeries, which, actually, are so well done, as to make each of these books an 'item' in itself in the world of collectors."

"Nevertheless," I said, but subsided into silence, not quite convinced, and feeling obscurely certain that Pons had not given an inch.

"I understand, Parker," said Pons with unaccustomed gentleness. "We would all like our world composed of black and white or right and wrong, but unfortunately matters are not as simple as all that. Would that they were! But if they were, how infernally dull life would be!"

27 January 1920

Coming in from attendance on a patient this evening, I found Pons absorbed in his crime files. Clippings from the newspapers, tearsheets from magazines and books, and photographs of criminals lay upon and all around the table—a veritable encyclopedia of crime.

As I entered, he glanced at me through the smoke wreathing about him from his pipe. "Ah, I see by your almost fatuous expression that Mr. Simpkins is making a satisfactory recovery," he said.

I acknowledged that my patient was indeed improving and, having divested myself of my greatcoat—for the wind howled outside, and snow was in the air—I went around to look at what engaged his interest at the moment. He held in his hand an account of the death of Edwin Bartlett in Pimlico in 1886, for which his wife Adelaide had been charged with murder—and acquitted.

"Did she do it?" I asked.

"I think it likely. She was enamoured of the Reverend George Dyson, a young minister who was foolish enough to write poems to her—if one could call them poems. Listen to this bit of doggerel—" He quoted from the account of the trial at the Old Bailey.

" 'Who is it that hath burst the door
Unclosed the heart that shut before
And set her queenlike on its throne
And made its homage all her own—My Birdie.'

'My Birdie,' indeed! There are manifestly some unhappy human beings for whom the simulation of love is a disease."

"You are being cynical, Pons," I said.

"The follies committed for the sake of what some people call 'love' are positively incredible," reflected Pons, not without a certain relish. "And the domain of crime offers innumerable examples."

"Well, it is certain that Bartlett could hardly have swallowed a bottle of chloroform without extreme agony—it would have seared its way to his stomach."

"Yet somehow it got there," said Pons. "As one learned medical man remarked after the trial—'Now she's acquitted, she should tell us, in the interests of science, how she did it.' "

He put down the Bartlett account and took up another.

"And no area of human activity so aptly demonstrates the mawkish gullibility and stupidity of the innocent," Pons went on. "As an example, consider the case of Bruneau, the priest, who led a career of crime from the age of thirteen onward and, though caught stealing even in the seminary, was nevertheless ordained in the same year that Edwin Bartlett came to his end, and continued in his career of theft, robbery, fraud, arson, and lechery until it culminated in the murder of his superior, the Abbé Fricot, whom he battered about the head before pushing him into the rectory garden well to die. He was duly executed at Laval in 1894—but after his burial some pious fools fostered a legend that Fricot had been murdered by a woman caught in theft, who had subsequently confessed her crime to Bruneau and so sealed his lips—a tale so ridiculous and so utterly without foundation that one would have to be somewhat less than a moron to credit it; yet hundreds of people were gullible enough to believe it—people have a positive horror of the obvious—and Bruneau was held to be a saint and a martyr. Indeed, some imbeciles actually brought sick children to Bruneau's grave in the hope that the 'sacred' earth above the body of this murderer, who was without a single redeeming feature, might heal them!"

"Does it give you pleasure to read about these crimes?" I asked. "I have seen you at these files quite often."

Pons raised his eyebrows. "That has the sound of a clinical question, Parker."

"No, no, I am only curious," I protested.

"Let us just say then that I find these accounts instructive."

"In what way?"

"Why, in reaffirming my low opinion of the rationality of the average individual, criminal or otherwise—or my alternatively dim view or high regard for the blundering or, on the other hand, the efficiency of the police—or my admiration for a crime well conceived and well investigated. Will that satisfy your curiosity, clinical or otherwise?"

I assured him that it adequately answered my inquiry.

"Though it is true that the average crime is without imagination," Pons continued, there are those that offer some interesting points. Consider the infinite trouble to which the pathetic Dr. Hawley Crippen went in order to indulge his passion for Ethel Le Neve! This was, incidentally, one of the earliest cases in which Spilsbury shone as medical examiner."

"Was it not also the first case of a British murderer's having been apprehended in America by dint of the police taking a faster boat?"

"No, no, that is a common misconception. It seems to have been the first time the wireless was used to apprehend a murderer. But Franz Müller, the first known train murderer—he killed Thomas Briggs in a train between Bow and Hackney Wick in the summer of 1864 and threw the body out on to the line—was apprehended as he stepped from the *Victoria* in New York, Tanner, the detective, having taken the faster ship, *City of Manchester.*"

He dropped the clipping and picked up a magazine account. "Now here is a classic American case—a miscarriage of justice—that of Lizzie Borden, who was acquitted of murdering her father and stepmother in Fall River, Massachusetts, on a hot day in August, 1892."

"I know the case," I said.

"I find the doggerel written about Lizzie much more to my fancy than set down by the Reverend Dyson for Adelaide Bartlett—

'Lizzie Borden took an axe,
And gave her mother forty whacks.
When she saw what she had done,
She gave her father forty-one.'

—And much more appropriate, too."

"You have no doubt of her guilt?"

"None. She alone had motive and opportunity. All other theories are the most elaborate fabrications, a testimony rather to the lubricity and wilful imagination of their authors, than to the inescapable facts of the matter. It is another incidence of people refusing to accept the obvious; for some reason they are infected by chronic doubt of what seems to them too simple, too straightforward; they prefer something more devious, more romantically sinister. The lunatic antics of the irrational skeptics in such cases are not without amusement. —But enough. I have had my fill of this entertainment for this evening."

As he gathered up the clippings and cuttings, he added reflectively, "Still and all, I suppose there is no domain of human behavior that so well illustrates the complex nature of man as that borderland in which he is impelled toward murder."

Solar Pons, Off-Trail

ONE JANUARY day in 1953 Mack Reynolds submitted to *The Magazine of Fantasy and Science Fiction* a Holmesian pastiche entitled *The Case of the Snitch in Time.* Editors Anthony Boucher and J. Francis McComas read the tale, and, in describing it in a letter to The Agent, McComas pronounced it "a story with a brilliant idea—that Sherlock Holmes is visited, via time machine, by a visitor from an alternate time-space continuum and solves a problem for said visitor. This is a honey of a plot; it combines beautifully the possibilities of a wondrous Holmes pastiche and a perfect science fiction story." But, on the distaff side, Mack Reynolds "did not in any sense of the word recreate Holmes, Watson or Baker Street."

In his letter of January 19 of that year McComas set forth the proposal made to Mack Reynolds. "We wrote to him, suggesting in general a collaboration with some stauch Irregular; in particular, we urged his OK on approaching you with the thought of working it out as a Solar Pons story. Mack sent along an enthusiastic affirmative. I quote: 'I'd appreciate it if you'd give Augie Derleth first chance at it. It was after reading his Solar Pons stories that I got the idea for *Snitch.* Besides that, I'm an admirer of the old Seigneur of Sauk City and it would be a privilege to have a story appear under a collaborative byline.' It would also be a privilege," added McComas, "for this magazine to be able to publish one more Solar Pons story—one with a strong science fiction theme."

Both Mack Reynolds and the editors were pleased with the Pontine tale that came from Reynolds's "brilliant idea". Anthony Boucher suggested a few small alterations which could be made in the office, and *The Adventure of the Snitch in Time* made its bow in the July, 1953 issue of *The Magazine of Fantasy and Science Fiction,* with, in part, this introduction:

"In a foreword to *Three Problems for Solar Pons,* Mr. Derleth sadly announced that Dr. Parker had, for personal reasons, decided to terminate his literary career. However, a kindly Fate has intervened to upset these plans of agent and author. A Mr. Mack Reynolds, while browsing in the archives of certain space-time continua, stumbled on a cryptic reference (in a most unlikely era) to Mr. Solar Pons. Careful research elicited the broad outlines of what is possibly the greatest triumph of the Pontine powers. Mr. Reynolds consulted Mr. Derleth; Mr. Derleth conferred with Dr. Parker; so persuasive was the agent (as agents should be) that the good Doctor was prevailed upon to give us one more adventure, the complete story of the one truly science fictional problem ever faced by the great detective."

By this time, Reynolds had come up with a second off-trail Pontine story titled *The Adventure of the Mad Dogs of Tomorrow*—another challenge to The Agent. This became *The Adventure of the Ball of Nostradamus,* and it, too, passed muster with the editors of *The Magazine of Fantasy and Science Fiction.* But its appearance was delayed—too much material lay in the files of the magazine for publication—and the story did not appear until the issue for June, 1955. In a sense this delay was fatal, for at least half a dozen off-trial stories had been projected between us—a third had actually been submitted to the magazine, but the editors took a dim view of it, and so did the agent. A fourth—titled *The Adventure of the Extra-Terrestrial*—had also come in, and languished in the files waiting on publication of the second pastiche.

When that publication came, our ardor had cooled—at one story every two years in the magazine, it would take a dozen years to accomplish publication of half a dozen stories. The project, interesting and challenging as it was, was not so much forthrightly abandoned as left to wither away.

*The Adventure of the Snitch in Time**

ON AN AUTUMN afternoon of a year that, for manifest reasons, must remain nameless, there came to the attention of my friend, Mr. Solar Pons, a matter which was surely either the most extraordinary adventure ever to befall a private enquiry agent in or before our time, or an equally extraordinary misadventure, the *raison d'etre* of which remains obscure even now, though it might have been born in the circumstances of the moment, for it was one of those days on which London was literally swallowed in a yellow fog, and we had both been confined to our quarters for two days, with no more incident than the arrival of an occasional paper and the unfailing complaint of our long-suffering landlady about Pons's spare appetite.

Even our warm and comfortable quarters, for all that a fire burned at the hearth, had begun to pall on us. Pons had exhausted the microscope; he had abandoned his chemistry set; he had ceased his abominable pistol practise; and for once there was not a single item of correspondence transfixed to the center of the mantelpiece by his knife. He had hardly stopped his restless wandering among the disorderly order of our quarters, and seated himself in his velvet-lined chair, holding forth on the points of difference between Stradivarius and Amati violins, when he rose once more with his empty pipe in his hands.

He was at the fireplace, about to take the shag from the toe of his slipper, tackled below the mantelpiece, when suddenly, he paused. He stood so for a moment, in utter silence, his

* With Mack Reynolds

hawklike face keen with interest, his body seeming actually to lean forward as if to catch the sound that smote upon his ears.

"If I am not mistaken, Parker," he said with unaccustomed gravity, "we are about to have a most unusual visitor."

I had been standing at the window looking out, and had just turned. "Nothing has disturbed this fog for the past half hour," I protested.

"My dear Parker, you are looking in the wrong direction. The footsteps are approaching from out there, and a little above."

So saying, he turned to face the door with alert expectation in his gray eyes.

I had for some time been conscious of a curious sound, almost as of water sliding at regular intervals against the roof. Apparently this was what Pons had mistaken for the sound of footsteps. Almost at the same moment of this realization, a most peculiar assault was made on the door to our quarters. I had not heard the outer door; in truth, I had heard no step upon the stair. But now a kind of brushing sound broke in upon us; it began at the top of the door, and did not become a recognizable knock until it had descended to midpanel.

Being nearest the door, I moved to open it.

"Pray be cautious, Parker," said Pons. "And spare me your alarm. Unless I am in egregrious error, our visitor is from another world."

I gazed at him, mouth agape. I had heard and marveled at his extraordinary deductions before, but this came from his lips with such calm assurance that I could not doubt his sincerity even while I could not accept his words.

"Come, Parker, let us not keep him waiting."

I threw open the door. There, confronting us, was a strong, healthy man, bronzed by the sun, clad in a fantastic attire of such brilliant hues as to dazzle the eye. His footgear—a strange combination of sandal and slipper—must have made the curious slapping sounds I had at first mistaken for the dripping of water, but which Pons had correctly identified as footsteps, however alien to our previous experience.

Our visitor looked briefly at me and said, "Ah, the famous literary doctor, I presume?" and smiled, as if in jest.

My astonishment at this manner of address, accompanied as it was with an almost insolent amusement, left me momentarily speechless.

"Come in, come in, my dear fellow," said Pons behind me. "Pray overlook Dr. Parker's rudeness. I perceive you have come a long way; your fatigue is manifest. Sit here and relieve yourself of the problem which brings you to these quarters."

Our visitor walked into the room, inclining his head to acknowledge Pon's invitation.

"I hope you will forgive my coming without an appointment," he said, in a somewhat stilted voice, accompanied by florid and Victorian gestures. "I fear I had no alternative. Let me introduce myself—I am Agent Tobias Athelney of the Terra Bureau of Investigation, Planet Terra, of the Solar System League."

Pons' eyes twinkled merrily.

"My dear sir," I could not help interrupting, "levity is all very well, but this is neither the time nor the place for it. Just where are you from?"

Our visitor had taken the seat to which Pons had waved him. At my words, he stopped short, took a small, violet-covered notebook from an inner fold of his robelike costume, and thumbed through it until he found the place he sought.

"Pray forgive me," he murmured. "If we were still using your somewhat fantastic calendar system, it would be the year 2565 A. D."

Pons, who had been scrutinizing him closely, now leaned back, closed his eyes, and touched his fingertips together. "So you represent yourself as a governmental agent of almost 700 years in the future, Mr. Athelney?" he said. "A traveler in time?"

Our visitor grimaced. "Not exactly, Mr. Pons. To my knowledge, there is no such thing as time travel, nor can such travel ever be developed. No, the explanation for my presence here is more elementary. We have recently discovered that the universe is not, indeed, one, but of an infinite number. We have learned that everything that possibly *could* happen *has* happened, *will* happen, and *is* happening. Given an infinite number of alternative universes, you can easily understand how this would be so. To illustrate, Mr. Pons, there are alternate spacetime continua in which Napoleon won at Waterloo; there are still others in which Waterloo was a draw; and there are yet others in which the battle was never fought at all—indeed, in which Napoleon was never born!"

I flashed a glance of mounting indignation at Pons, but my companion's face had taken on that dream expression I had learned to associate with intense concentration. Surely it could not be that he was being deceived by this patent mountebank!

"Infinite other universes than this," murmured Pons, "containing other persons identical to myself, and to Dr. Parker, here, who carry on their little lives in much the same manner as we do?"

Our visitor nodded. "That is correct, Mr. Pons. There are still other spacetime continua, in which there are no such persons as yourselves, never have been, and never will be." He coughed almost apologetically. "In fact, in this multitude of alternate universes, Mr. Pons, there are some in which you two are fictitious characters, the product of a popular writer's art!"

"Amazing!" exclaimed Pons, adding, with a glance at my dour face, "and yet, not entirely incredible, would you say, Parker?"

"Preposterous!" I answered. "How can you sit there and calmly accept this—this nonsense?"

"Dear me," murmured Pons, "let us not be too hasty, Parker."

"I am sorry to have upset Dr. Parker," said our visitor soberly, "but it is from just such a universe that I have traveled to this. Approximately 700 years before my birth, in my space-time continuum, a series of stories dealing with Mr. Solar Pons and Dr. Lyndon Parker were written, presumably by Dr. Parker, and became the all-time favorites of the literature of deduction."

"Let us assume all this is so," said Pons. "For what purpose have you come?"

"To consult you, Mr. Pons."

"I fancied as much," said my companion with a serene smile. "Though it would seem a long chance indeed to consult a fictitious character."

"*Touché!*" answered our client. "But a fictitous character in *my* universe and 700 years before my time. But in *this* universe you are very real indeed, and the greatest detective of all time!" He sighed. "You cannot imagine, Mr. Pons, the difficulty of first finding a continuum in which you were *real,* and then, on top of that, one in which you were contemporary."

Pons sat for a moment in silence, stroking the lobe of his left ear. "I submit," he said at last, "since patterns of crime and its detection continually evolve, you are haunting the wrong continuum, Mr. Athelney."

"I think not, Mr. Pons, if you will hear me out."

"Proceed."

"One of our most scientifically advanced bands of criminals is named the Club Cerise, after the favorite color of its leader, Moriarty. They—"

"Moriarty!" exclaimed Pons.

"Yes, Mr. Pons. Moriarty. The name is familiar to you perhaps?"

"Indeed it is!" Pons was silent for a moment, his eyes closed. "You know, Parker," he said after a moment, "I have always felt that one death at the Reichenbach was as false as the other." He sat up in his chair, his gaze now intent on our visitor. "Pray continue, Mr. Athelney! Where my illustrious predecessor could achieve but a stalemate, it seems that you offer me the opportunity for complete victory!"

"Well, then, Mr. Pons," our visitor resumed, "you will not be surprised to learn that Moriarty and his band have managed to escape retribution for some time, and it is in regard to their apprehension that I seek your assistance. The criminal method they have developed is based on the same discovery that allows my presence here. Moriarty and his Club Cerise have been making a practice of invading space-time continua in less developed eras than our own, and, utilizing our most advanced weapons and devices to assure their escape, have been despoiling these universes of their art treasures. Not long ago, for example, they went into a Twentieth Century universe and obtained a Da Vinci, a half dozen Rembrandts, and a priceless collection of Kellys."

Pons' eyes widened a trifle. "You are suggesting that the Irish have developed an artist of the stature of Da Vinci, Mr. Athelney?"

"Indeed, yes. A fellow named Kelly created a work of genius called *Pogo,* which appeared in hundreds of newspapers of his day. These were *Pogo* originals, including some of the very rare pre-strip drawings. With his fabulously valuable treasure, Moriarty and his band managed to return to our own space-time continuum. Obviously, we cannot punish them in our universe, since they have committed no crime there. Under ordinary circumstances, it would be possible to extradite them to the universe they plundered—but there are almost insurmountable complications."

Pons smiled, still giving no evidence of being in the slightest troubled by the mad, ingenious, account of our prospective client. "I daresay 'insurmountable' is the word to describe the problems attendant upon extradition of a group of criminals from a country which doesn't exist in the universe where the crime was committed. I submit that a Twentieth Century nation might be compelled to adopt extraordinary protective measures—if indeed these would be adequate—to deal with criminals seven centuries in advance of the police of that period." But now he shook his head, with a gentle smile on his thin lips. "But we must stop considering these ramifications, or we shall soon find ourselves involved in the higher mathematics of space and time."

"The importance of the problem is greater than might at first be evident," continued our visitor. "Given continued success on the part of Moriarty and his Club Cerise, there can be no doubt that other such bands will soon emulate them, and that eventually endless numbers of space-time pirates will give up other pursuits to devote themselves to the plundering of weaker continua with this type of snitch."

"Snitch?" I repeated.

"Elementary, Parker," murmured Pons impatiently. "Obviously idiomatic for 'theft'."

"The ultimate possibility will not have escaped you, Mr. Pons," continued our client. "Sooner or later, the increasing numbers of criminals would arrive in *this* space-time continuum and in *this* era."

I could not be sure, but it seemed to me that at this suggestion a little color drained from Pons' cheecks. And, if a shudder went through that lean frame, he was again under perfect control within moments. He sat then in silence, his eyes closed, his head sunk to his chest with his fingertips gently tapping together.

Our visitor waited in silence.

Pons opened his eyes presently and asked, "Pray tell me, Mr. Athelney—do you have income taxes in your world?"

Athelney groaned. "My dear fellow, last year my taxes were unbelievably high. Bureaucracy runs rampant!"

"Capital, capital!" exclaimed Pons. "Why not prosecute Moriarty for tax evasion?"

Our visitor shook his head dolefully. "The criminals of our days are advanced, Mr. Pons. They *pay* their taxes."

Once again Pons retreated into silence, taking time now to light up his calabash. But this time his silence was broken more quickly.

"I have some modest knowledge of British law, Mr. Athelney," said Pons, "but your laws may well differ. What type of social system prevails in your world and time?"

"It is usually referred to as Industrial Feudalism."

"I am not familiar with the term, though I can guess its meaning. Pray elucidate."

"In the same manner that Feudalism evolved from Chattel Slavery, and Capitalism from Feudalism, so Industrial Feudalism has evolved in our continuum from Capitalism. Ownership has contracted until a few princes of finance, a few industrial barons and lords of transportation completely control the government and practically all the wealth."

"Do national boundaries still prevail,"

"Terra is united, but we have loose ties with the other planets of the Solar System."

"Then doubtless you have tariff laws between the various planets."

"Very rigid ones. Last month we apprehended some Martians smuggling duppl berries; they were given ten years."

"I submit you have an obvious trap in which to take Moriarty and his Club Cerise, Mr. Athelney. They must pay import taxes on those art objects. Failure to do so puts them afoul of the law."

Our client smiled broadly. "I do believe, Mr. Pons, you have arrived at a solution of our problem."

He came to his feet.

"I suggest your government pass such tariff restrictions as to make imports from other space-time continua prohibitive. Such a move, in view of the fact that the criminals of your time are so advanced as to pay their taxes, would in all likelihood prevent further depredations."

Though our client was manifestly anxious to be off, he hesitated. "I wish there were some way in which I could remunerate you, Mr. Pons. Unfortunately, we do not use the same system of exchange. All I can do is offer profound thanks in the name of my continuum."

"There is surely remuneration enough implied in the promise that we will not be victimized here in our time and world by such as Moriarty," said Pons. "But, stay, Mr. Athelney—I perceive you are still troubled by some aspect of the matter."

Our client turned from the threshold, to which he had walked. He smiled wryly. "I fear, Mr. Pons, that this is but the initial step in our problem. Moriarty, when he learned I was to travel hither in search of the greatest detective of all time, took certain protective measures. He sent one of his own men to another space-time continuum to acquire the services of a most astute lawyer named Randolph Mason."

"Pray be reassured," responded Pons instantly. "I can refer you to a rising young contemporary, who promises to be even greater, and is gaining a challenging reputation in the legal circles of his world. By an odd coincidence, not uncommon to fiction, be bears a similar family name. His given name, I believe, is Perry. My correspondents on the west coast of the United States have given me flattering reports of his talents. You will find him in Los Angeles, I believe. I commend him to your government. Good afternoon, Mr. Athelney."

As soon as the door had closed behind our visitor, I turned to Pons. "Should not one of us slip after him and notify the authorities of his escape?"

Pons walked to the window and looked out into the fog. Without turning, he asked, "You thought him a lunatic, Parker?"

"Surely that was ovious!"

"Was it, indeed!" Pons shook his head. "I sometimes think, Parker, that that happy faculty for observation which seems to come so readily to me encounters obstacles of demoralizing stubbornness in you."

"Pons!" I exclaimed hotly, "you cannot have been taken in by this—this mountebank and his hoax?"

"Was he both lunatic and mountebank, then?" asked Pons, smiling in that superior manner which always galled me.

"What does it matter which he was? He was certainly one or the other."

"If a mountebank, what was his motive? If a lunatic, how did he find his way here in this fog, which is surely as thick as any we have ever had? I fear some of us have an unhappy tendency to dismiss the incredible solely because it is incredible to *us*. Tell me, Parker, have you ever contemplated setting forth in the form of fiction these little adventures of mine in the field of ratiocination?"

I hesitated to answer.

"Come, come, Parker, it is evident that you have."

"I confess, I have thought of it."

"You have not yet done so?"

"No, Pons, I swear it."

"You have spoken of your plans to no one?"

"No."

"Our late client spoke of you as a literary doctor. 'The famous literary doctor' were his exact words, I believe. If he were but a lunatic or mountebank, as you will have him, how came he then to know of your innermost hope and ambition in this regard? Or is there some secret communion between lunatics and mountebanks? I perceive, thanks to our Mr. Athelney that, without regard to my wishes, you are destined to become a literary man at the expense of my modest powers."

"Pons, I swear I have never put pen to paper," I cried.

"But you will, Parker, you will. May I remind you of my distinguished predecessor's credo, that when all probable explanations have been shown false, the improbable, no matter how incredible, alone remains? This, I fancy, is one little adventure you will not be able to chronicle without a furtive blush or two.'

In this, at least, my companion was correct.

*The Adventure of the Ball of Nostradamus**

MY FRIEND, SOLAR PONS, the private enquiry agent, has a tendency to be highly dubious of all coincidence—but was it only coincidence that he should refer to the singular adventure of the late Abraham Weddigan on the very day that I had determined to set down the facts about this horrible affair which shocked a continent and, on its successful termination, brought Pons the profound gratitude of millions of people as well as the personal felicitations of His Majesty? From the moment of its conclusion, Pons began to entertain some doubt about Abraham Weddigan, that strange, unforgettable monster—a description of my own which Pons will not countenance—and soon his doubts grew, so that often, when I saw him sitting in profound and troubled thought, and knew no problem had come in to enlist his keen mind, I was aware that he was once again pondering the meaning of the motives of Abraham Weddigan.

On that day in the 1920's that Pons entered the case, in the second decade of our sharing his quarters at Number 7B, Praed Street, I had been reading about the murder of a child—the second in the streets of London. Pons was standing at the window, his long thin hands clasped behind his back, his eyes fastened on the street below.

"I observe that you, too, my dear Parker," said Pons suddenly, without turning, "have begun to wonder—not without some indignation—about the child-murderer in our midst."

"How could you know which account I was reading?" I asked in surprise.

* With Mack Reynolds

He turned, his ascetic face briefly alight with a smile. "My dear fellow, surely it is elementary. You are agitated, you rustle your paper indignantly, you squirm your disapproval of the police methods in the case, indeed, you all but snort in irritation. What else in the morning paper could stir to such indignation a man who has always been interested in the crime life of London?"

"Ah, you have read of it then!"

"You know my habits, Parker. Little escapes me."

He came over to stuff his pipe with shag from the slipper tacked to the mantel-piece, and sat down in his favorite chair, a frown on his high forehead.

"I fear I neglected to tell you," he went on, "but I am expecting our friend Jamison at any moment. He sent word by messenger this morning before you awoke that he wished to see me on the matter, and it is now some minutes past the hour set for his arrival. Since he is customarily so prompt, I fancy some new facts may have come to light."

"Or another child murder," I put in.

"God forbid! This shocking chain of child murders is far more extensive than Inspector Jamison may know." He listened a moment and added, "But there is the police car now, if I am not mistaken, arriving in Jamison's usual haste."

The outer door opened and closed violently, and Jamison came up the stairs as rapidly as his rotund bulk would permit.

"Dear me," murmured Pons, "I would far rather Jamison glum than Jamison in such good spirits."

I opened the door to Jamison and saw that he was indeed in good spirits, for a broad smile sprang into being on his chubby face, his eyes twinkled, and his mustache fairly trembled with delight at sight of us.

"This time, Pons, we have done it without you!"

"My congratulations! But what is it you have done?"

"We have our man for the murder of Terence Allen and Thomas Kanczeny."

"The child murderer!" I cried. "I thought the crimes clueless."

"Ah, so they were," Jamison went on, rubbing his hands together. "We did not set out to arrest Captain Martin Verne for murder—we went only to question him."

"Pray begin at the beginning, Jamison," interrupted Pons patiently.

"Very well. I need not go into detail about the crimes themselves; you are familiar enough with the shocking shooting-down of two defenseless children on the city streets. We have been interested—remotely, it is true—in the activities of Captain Martin Verne—"

"One-time soldier of fortune, gun runner, assassin for hire, last heard of in Morocco, after some years in Nicaragua, in China, and on the Continent," said Pons.

"That's him. Well, Pons, he's our man. When he came to England three months ago, he was living close to the bone. We knew as much, and spread the word that the Yard was interested in Verne. So one day he moved from the hole he lived in out Wapping way, set himself up in Park Lane, no less, new wardrobe, and new night life—all the more expensive restaurants and theaters. A nark passed us the word, and two men went over last night to ask him some questions. Verne must have suspected they were after something elese. He tried to put them off, then he tried to shoot his way out. He put a bullet into Police Constable MacEachern's shoulder, but Constable Leeds put him out with his truncheon. Leeds hit him harder than he ought to have done, and Verne died half an hour ago. But not before we got down what he said in delirium; and when we had him conscious for a little while before the end, and put it to him: did he kill the children?—he admitted it. Further, the laboratory tests show that a bullet from his gun killed the Allen boy: no bullet was recovered in the case of Kanczeny. So there we are."

Pons had listened with keen interest. Now, however, his eyes, darkened, his frown returned. "And the motive?"

"He had no time for that. Still, we thought it might be in what he said. You see, the moment they heard him talking, they started taking down what he said. I wasn't called in until after I'd sent word to you. One look at what they'd taken down, and I knew Verne was our man. I brought along a copy of it for you, Pons. You've done me a good many favors in the past."

He took a folded paper from his inner coat pocket as he spoke and handed it to Pons. It was hardly the size of an ordinary sheet of manuscript paper and was, as I saw when I rose and walked over to look from behind Pons, little more than a meaningless jumble of disjointed sentences. Nevertheless, Pons read it with the keenest interest, though for my part I failed to see that Verne's utterances in delirium conveyed anything of signal importance. The typescript was commendably short.

Terence Allen, aged 9 . . . Escape tutor . . . the ball knows . . . savior o' the world . . . That damned fortune-teller! . . . two hundred gross of Brens . . . Look, sir, it's a bit out o' me line . . . first the smoke, then the picture . . . Christ! how real it is . . . Bloddy old Mussolini! . . . Thomas Kanczeny, Hungarian legation, seven years old . . . mad dog, mad dog, mad dog . . . Gentlemen, we aims to quarantine, if you please, to prevent . . . blast him forever! putting the blood o' kids on me hands! . . . A pound never looked better to me, and that's the truth, so help me God, but I didn't bargain for that kind of blood money . . . Guns you ordered and guns you got; I'll look at the color o' your money . . . Touch the ball, Mister. Fifty quid to have your fortune told. Knows all, sees all, tells the future, tells the past. Fifty quid, Mister . . . My alibi's perfect. Nobody can touch me but me . . . And if I wasn't so bad off for money, I'd never take on a dirty job like this . . . Guns is my line, sir, guns and contraband. I'm the best."

Pons looked up, his eyes fairly dancing.

"Couldn't have made it clearer in a signed confession," said Jamison, smiling happily. "We know the Allen boy was shot when he ran away from his tutor. Now, just to corroborate, we've sent a man out to discover whether there was a dog at or near the scene, plainly enough in evidence, when the Kanczeny boy was killed."

"And how do you plan to establish the connecting link with —let us choose at random—the death of little Ossip Ciciorka in Prague four months ago?" interposed Pons quietly.

Jamison's mouth fell agape. His joviality faded; he grew wary. "Of whom?" he asked finally.

Pons repeated the name and added, "Or, for that matter, of Georges Murat, aged ten, in the Rue d'Auseil, Paris, on May ninth last year; of Giovanni d'Orsini, aged eight, on a holiday in Naples two years ago; of Timor Gushenko, aged six, on the beach of Cannes with his parents three years ago; or even of the abortive attempt on the life of Ana Rabinsohn, a girl of five, in the streets of Bucharest six years ago."

Jamison had recovered his composure. "Pons, you are joking. And an ill-conceived joke it is," said he.

"I daresay you would think so. I regret that it is no jest. I have never been more in earnest. Let us pause for a moment and examine into the matter. There are striking parallels I believe you cannot fail to apprehend. In neither the Allen nor the Kanczeny case was any attempt to kidnap made."

"No."

"Nor to collect blackmail from the parents of these unfortunate victims."

"No."

"Nor was there any molestation of the children themselves."

"No."

"In both these instances murder alone would seem to have been the object of the attack."

"Quite so. It was in all the papers."

"The pattern is precisely similar to their continental predecessors. All are unsolved crimes. And, of even greater importance, they are seemingly without motive. Or did you discover at the last hour with Verne any trace of one?"

Jamison flushed.

"Ah, you need not answer. I submit, then, that Verne had been hired to commit at least these last two crimes. He may have had a hand in some of the others, but I am inclined to doubt it. Very well then. If not Verne, some other hired assassin. They abound in Europe; each has his price, and most may have been less squeamish than Verne. I put it to you that no one pays a hired assassin to murder a child without some motive, however obscure. No, do not say it Jamison—the psychopath does not hire murder done; he does it himself. We must cast into other waters for our motive, Jamison."

"When word of Verne's death reaches whoever it was who hired him, I'll wager he'll leave London by the fastest means," said Jamison.

"Dear me, I had not thought that Scotland Yard was less intent upon the capture of a murderer than his flight beyond their jurisdiction. I fancy that concept of crime detection will interest the Commissioner."

"Oh, come, Pons, you are taking me too literally. Depend on it, we shall be on the watch for him. But, I confess, we have not the slightest hint of motive."

"I suspected as much," said Pons dryly. "But the picture is not so hopeless as all that, surely. There are several salient facts which are curiously similar in the majority of the murders."

"You believe that those you have mentioned are connected with these in London?"

"Can you doubt it? Consider: the methods in all cases are exactly similar, and so are the circumstances surrounding them. There is a sinister pattern in the very fact that there is no similarity whatsoever—unless we are unable to see it—among the victims of this plague of murder. Those children come from all walks of life. Allen was the son of a poor laborer. Kanczeny belonged to parents in the Hungarian embassy. Cicioka was the son of a Polish librarian. Young d'Orsini, though of an ancient Italian family, was the son of an artist, Murat of a wine merchant, Gushenko of a petty railroad official. And the abortive attempt in Bucharest was made on the daughter of humble Jewish parents.

"Murder of children for vengeance against the parents is not unknown; it was practised at one time by the Maffia. But it is highly unlikely that these murders have a common origin of that nature; they are too widely separated to make it probable that one terror organization could be responsible for these crimes, and to presuppose others is to enter the realm of pure conjecture without relation to facts. None of the parents involved is important enough to have incurred political enmities. Indeed, they are nonentities—even Kanczeny's position at the embassy is that of a minor clerk. In almost every instance, the children were murdered at a supremely felicitous moment for the murderer—when they had strayed or run away, which suggests either a constant watchfulness or an uncanny knowledge. I venture to suggest that all these crimes were the work of one guiding genius."

"A Napoleon of crime," cried Jamison.

"You do Napoleon's memory no service. A modern Herod, perhaps." Pons made an impatient gesture. "But we are wasting time. I beg you to stand by, Jamison. I mean to find the author of these crimes."

When Jamison had gone, Pons turned to me. "If you were to need the services of a fortune-teller—surely one of position, who asks 'fifty quid' a reading—to whom in all London would you apply?"

"Elementary, my deal Pons!" I cried. "There is surely but one such seer: the consultant—so he terms himself—visited by peers, M. P.'s, even persons close to the court—Abraham Wedigan. His fees are exorbitant, and he is never at a loss for patrons."

But Pons was already looking into a London directory. "Let us see. Ah, here we are. His office is in Southampton Row. Let us lose no time. We shall start with him. If we are in error, we shall carry on from there. None knows to what lengths he may be driven now that his hireling is dead."

"Are you not taking the delirium of a dying man too seriously?" I inquired when at last we were in a cab rolling toward Southampton Row.

Pons sat in his accustomed pose, head sunk to his chest, the fingers of one hand toying with the lobe of his right ear, his eyes clouded and dark, fixed on a point not in space but in time.

"No, no," he said impatiently. "I submit that the last words of Verne, however disjointed, nevertheless pointed clearly to some baleful connection with a fortune-teller. 'That damned fortune-teller!' he said. And twice more, he made reference to 'the ball'—which surely is the crystal globe so much an integer in the impedimenta of the seer. We are quite safe in eliminating the references to guns and gun-running; these would be bound to show up in such a scattering of memories as the situation implies. I submit we are on the right track. 'Fifty quid' for a reading. No small sum. No crossing of the palm with mere silver. No indeed. 'Fifty quid'—and for that someone who knows all and sees all will tell the past and the future. Verne had become obsessed by him—and by the magic ball—to such an extent that a rudimentary conscience made him try to flee when, in actuality, none pursued him, and so brought him to his death."

Abraham Weddigan's suite of offices was in one of the most modern buildings on Southampton Row, one given over to business offices representing some of the foremost industries in all England. There, as sedate as any other, Abraham Weddigan was duly listed as a Consultant, and his suite was no secret.

We mounted to his floor, found his number, and were prepared to knock when the door was opened noiselessly from wthin. There before us stood a Caucasian of dark complexion, a Mauritanian, surely. He wore a turban and complementary clothing. He bowed.

"Mr. Solar Pons and Dr. Lyndon Parker. Step this way, if you please, sirs. The Master is expecting you."

"We made no appointment," I said with asperity.

"The Master knows all save his own fate," said the Mauritanian. "Such is as it was ordained."

He led us down a short corridor to a wide door at its end. There he stood, his head bowed, making no sound.

Nevertheless, a voice from within called out, "Enter."

The Mauritanian threw open the door and stood aside for us to enter a large, almost unfurnished room. In its center was a low divan; opposite it, a conventional but luxurious easy chair. Between chair and divan rose a small round table of oriental manufacture, supporting a small crystal ball. The occupant of the chair came to his feet and motioned to the divan.

"Mr. Pons, Doctor Parker—pray be seated."

His hands were fine and soft, as delicate as a woman's; his eyes were deep and lustrous; his gray hair was heavy and worn long, the only factor of his appearance that seemed affected, for his dress was conventional—a gray business suit. He was a compelling, extraordinarily handsome man, however old he might have been. As he resumed his seat, Pons and I sat on the divan.

"We came . . ." began Pons, but Weddigan held up his hand for silence.

"I regret the nature of your call. I regret the circumstances which have brought it about. The children, yes. The crystal told me Verne was not efficient. Now he is dead before my work in London is finished. Shall I go elsewhere to pursue it? I cannot say; the crystal is dark, very dark."

"Do you now confess to having compelled the man Verne to murder two defenseless children?" I demanded.

"Gently, gently, Parker," admonished Pons, laying a restraining hand on my arm. "We shall listen to Mr. Weddigan."

Weddigan inclined his head. "Thank you, Mr. Pons. Fate has implacably determined that we must be opposed to each other. I regret that circumstance. I know you will hinder my plans. How shall I speak of them to you?" An expression of great weariness came into his face, and he shook his head slowly from side to side. "Have I any other course? I think not, gentlemen. I hope and pray that you are not of the race of doubters and the army of the Philistines. I have the gift of true precognition." He laid one hand on the crystal ball before him. "All the myths of mankind, gentlemen, have a root, however remote, in fact—even the dream of seeing man's future in a crystal ball. This is no ordinary crystal, believe me. It is old, very old—it and the strangely wrought base of silver on which it stands. The inscriptions are in Sumerian cuneiform characters. It was ancient before the city of Ur. Of its origin I have no knowledge, but many years ago, in the year 1550, a traveler from Greece, who had found this crystal in the ruins of Delphi, sold it to a Frenchman named Michel de Nostredame."

"The crystal ball of Nostradamus," murmured Pons.

"At least he is not strange to you, Mr. Pons. And was not Nostradamus the most famous seer of all time? Did not his prophecies, one upon another, come true—centuries after he had set them down?"

"The fulfillment of prophecies, like beauty, is too often only in the eye of the beholder," replied Pons. "But I concede that the French physician offers as nearly adequate evidence for prevision as I know."

"This is the original crystal ball and from it stems the information you seek. It was because of what I saw in the future that it became necessary for me to serve my race by destroying the young persons in whom you are interested."

"You wish us to believe that you hired assassins—Verne in London, others elsewhere—to murder harmless children because of what you saw in the ball of Nostradamus?" asked Pons, shaking his head gently. "Sir, I am no seer; I am but an humble practitioner of the art of ratiocination. This is beyond reason."

"Indeed it is," agreed Weddigan. "I repeat it. These children, Ossip Ciciorka, Terence Allen, Timor Gushenko—but I need not name them; you know their names—these children, I say, were destined to become the oppressors, the dictators, the mad dogs of tomorrow, the Mussolinis of their generation, to fire the earth with war and pestilence, to subjugate and degrade mankind to its lowest level. I failed in the case of the girl, Ana Rabinsohn; perhaps I shall have opportunity to try it again. There is but one more in London—Josef Zollern. With your permission, I shall personally execute him."

"I regret our inability to aid your crime, Mr. Weddigan," said Pons.

"Stay a moment, sir. Will you look into the ball? Pray have no fear of chicanery. And you, Dr. Parker. And tell me in a moment or two what you see there."

Pons and I turned to the ball. And in a moment, scarcely more, the crystal had begun to cloud up, as if smoke had somehow entered the glass. I flashed a glance at our monstrous host, and saw him bent above the ball, his hands flat on either side of it, his head bowed, an expression of infinite sadness in his features. Then the ball drew me again, and I saw a scene beginning to take shape, as of a vast concourse of people, before whom stood a fair-haired young man wearing a scarlet tunic, haranguing them passionately and receiving their ovations. The impassioned orator bore a sabre-slash on his right cheek. All about hung the paraphernalia of tyranny. The scene held but briefly; then the clouds swirled up and it was gone.

"I know only too well what you saw, gentlemen," said Weddigan. He rose, clapping his hands.

The Mauritanian appeared almost instantly.

"Forgive me," said Weddigan, bowing once more, his eyes fixed upon some goal far beyond us. "I am an idealist, a perfectionist. I wear a curse upon my soul." And to the servant he said, "Detain Mr. Pons and Dr. Parker for twenty minutes. I leave to protect the future."

The seer stepped behind the servant and vanished into the dark hangings along the wall. The Mauritanian resolutely barred our way, standing with folded arms before us, his sudden menace to make of him a giant. And indeed, his shoulders were as broad as any I have seen, and his girth was in keeping. He weighed well over fifteen stone, and his aspect was formidable.

Neither of us made a move for several moments. Then suddenly Pons reached out, took up the crystal ball of Nostradamus, and at the same time came to his feet and flung the ball with all his might. The surprised Mauritanian fell without a cry, and the ball shattered when it struck the floor beyond the divan.

Pons leaped over the fallen servant and, without turning to see whether I was following, ran out into the hall to the elevators. In the foyer he found what he sought—a telephone directory of London.

"There is but one chance we may save the boy, Parker," he said. "Twenty minutes, Weddigan said. Let us see . . . Z . . . Zollern. Clapham, Loughborough, Norwood—these Zollerns are well over twenty minutes from Southampton Row. Camden Town. Count Helmut von and zu Zollern—he alone is within twenty minutes of these premises. Now, if only we can reach Jamison in time . . ."

We sped toward Camden Town in a fortuitously discovered cab, and turned into a middle-class residential street just as the tall figure of Abraham Weddigan passed the flats housing the Zollern family we sought.

"Slow down, driver," said Pons.

Weddigan, having reached the end of the street, turned to walk back.

At that moment a small figure emerged from the flats and started across the street. At sight of him, Weddigan changed his pace to swerve toward the boy.

"Now!" cried Pons. "Pray heaven we are not too late! Driver, get down there at once."

Just as the driver started up, a Flying Squad car raced

around the further corner and bore down upon Weddigan. The white face of Abraham Weddigan came up, his eyes widening as he saw the two cars coming toward him. His hand darted into his coat and brought out a stub-nosed pistol. He began to run toward the eleven-year-old.

The bulky figure of Inspector Jamison leaned from the window of the police car, heavy Webley in hand. Within the second it spoke sharply, once and again. Weddigan spun around and dropped to the street, his weapon skittering from his hand.

Pons, myself, and Jamison were out of our respective vehicles in a moment. We ran forward, while young Josef Zollern, who had turned at the excitement to look back, began to walk toward Weddigan's body. The four of us reached the scene almost together.

"Done in," said Jamison curtly. "Acting on your information, Pons. We've traced some of Verne's payments to Weddigan. A madman."

"It would seem so," replied Pons, gazing thoughtfully down at the fallen body. "Even if I find it difficult to forget how he spoke of Mussolini. There are more important things in government than making the trains run on time . . ."

Josef Zollern, a pale, pinch-faced youngster, looked down at the corpse almost with contempt. Momentarily, a fire seemed to flash in the depths in his dark eyes.

"Young man, you were in danger," said Jamison with bluff heartiness.

The boy's lips were touched with disdain.

"I suppose that before my destiny is fulfilled, I shall see a good deal of this," he said shrilly. There was a cutting edge of fanaticism in his voice.

Pons gazed at him as if he seen him for the first time.

The boy looked back with eyes that were proud and insolent. Then he turned and walked, quite self-possessed, back to the apartment house from which tenants were coming toward the scene.

Happily, that was the end of the inexplicable sequence of child murders which had shocked the Continent. With Weddigan's death, the case was closed, and so it is marked in the police files, despite Pon's annoying, "Only the future will tell, Parker."

Three thousand copies of this book have been printed by The Collegiate Press, George Banta Company, Inc., Menasha, Wisconsin, from Linotype Baskerville on Winnebago Eggshell. The binding cloth is Holliston Black Novelex.